D1481948

Thermophilic Fungi

A SERIES OF BOOKS IN BIOLOGY

Editors   DOUGLAS M. WHITAKER
RALPH EMERSON
DONALD KENNEDY
GEORGE W. BEADLE   (1946–1961)

Principles of Human Genetics   (Second Edition)
Curt Stern

Experiments in General Biology
Graham DuShane and David Regnery

Principles of Plant Physiology
James Bonner and Arthur W. Galston

General Genetics
Adrian M. Srb and Ray D. Owen

An Introduction to Bacterial Physiology   (Second Edition)
Evelyn L. Oginsky and Wayne W. Umbreit

Laboratory Studies in Biology: Observations and their Implications
Chester A. Lawson, Ralph W. Lewis, Mary Alice Burmester, and Garrett Hardin

Plants in Action: A Laboratory Manual of Plant Physiology
Leonard Machlis and John G. Torrey

Comparative Morphology of Vascular Plants
Adriance S. Foster and Ernest M. Gifford, Jr.

Taxonomy of Flowering Plants
C. L. Porter

Growth, Development, and Pattern
N. J. Berrill

Biology: Its Principles and Implications
Garrett Hardin

Animal Tissue Techniques
Gretchen L. Humason

Microbes in Action: A Laboratory Manual of Microbiology
Harry W. Seeley, Jr., and Paul J. VanDemark

Botanical Histochemistry: Principles and Practice
William A. Jensen

Modern Microbiology
Wayne W. Umbreit

Laboratory Outlines in Biology
Peter Abramoff and Robert G. Thomson

Molecular Biology of Bacterial Viruses
Gunther S. Stent

Principles of Numerical Taxonomy
Robert R. Sokal and Peter H. A. Sneath

Population, Evolution, and Birth Control: A Collage of Controversial Readings
Garrett Hardin, Editor

Plants in Perspective: A Laboratory Manual of Modern Biology
Eldon H. Newcomb, Gerald C. Gerloff, and William F. Whittingham

Thermophilic Fungi: An Account of Their Biology, Activities, and Classification
Donald G. Cooney and Ralph Emerson

Structure and Function in the Nervous Systems of Invertebrates
Theodore Holmes Bullock and G. Adrian Horridge

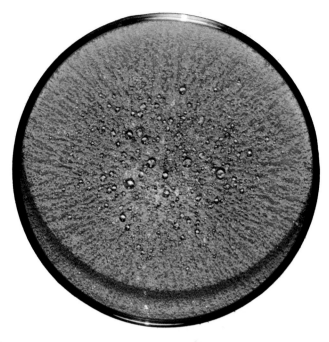

Thermoascus aurantiacus, 7 days at 37°C on oatmeal (OA) agar.

Malbranchea pulchella var. *sulfurea,* 8 days at 45°C
on yeast-glucose (YG) agar.

Thermophilic Fungi

AN ACCOUNT OF

THEIR BIOLOGY, ACTIVITIES,

AND CLASSIFICATION

Donald G. Cooney UNIVERSITY OF NEVADA

Ralph Emerson UNIVERSITY OF CALIFORNIA, BERKELEY

W. H. FREEMAN AND COMPANY
SAN FRANCISCO AND LONDON

WARNER MEMORIAL LIBRARY
EASTERN COLLEGE
ST. DAVIDS, PA. 19087

6/12/84

QK 604 .C66 1964
Cooney, Donald G.
Thermophilic fungi

© Copyright 1964 by W. H. Freeman and Company

The publisher reserves all rights to reproduce this book
in whole or in part, with the exception of the right to use
short quotations for review of the book

Library of Congress Catalog Card Number 64-21149

Printed in the United States of America

TO

Hugo Miehe

PIONEER INVESTIGATOR OF
THERMOPHILIC MICROORGANISMS
AND SELF-HEATING HAY

PREFACE

During the war years, 1944 to 1946, the second author (R.E.) had an unusual opportunity to become familiar with almost all the known thermophilic fungi. He was serving as Microbiologist, with Dr. Paul J. Allen, in the Guayule Rubber Extraction Research Unit of the United States Department of Agriculture at Salinas, California. The Microbiology Laboratory was engaged in a detailed investigation of guayule retting, a process in which the rubber-producing shrub, *Parthenium argentatum*, was subjected to microbial action in order to yield a rubber of improved quality. Microbial thermogenesis occurred in the retting guayule, just as in a manure or compost heap, and temperatures of 40°–60°C were commonly reached and maintained within the shrub mass. The heating and retting were brought about by a very mixed natural flora of microorganisms, including bacteria and Actinomycetes as well as true fungi. Thermophilic representatives of all three groups appeared in great profusion and were subjected to intensive study. It was in the course of this work that the first representatives of our own collection of thermophilic fungi were obtained. About half of the species to be discussed in the following pages came from this source.

The second phase of our investigations is represented by a comprehensive comparative study, as well as extensive additional collections and isolations, made by the first author (D.G.C.) during his research for the Ph.D. degree at the University of California, Berkeley. Our joint efforts permitted us to establish a collection of cultures that included all the previously known thermophilic fungi as well as four undescribed species and a number of new varieties.

Very possibly the several stages of this investigation should have been published at intervals as separate contributions. Certainly such a schedule would have made some of our results available at a much earlier date. In holding the entire contribution for publication as a coordinated whole at the present time, we are running counter to present publication trends, but we are expressing our belief that a unified, monographic treatment will have more comprehensive and lasting use.

It is our primary purpose to acquaint the reader with the special group of true fungi that have the capacity to grow at unusually high temperatures. Our account, therefore, is first and foremost for the mycologist, and more than half of the text is devoted to a detailed analysis of the morphology, development, systematics, and cultural behavior of this highly specialized segment of the microbial world. The more we have explored the activities of the thermophilic fungi, however, the more we have been impressed with their wide implications and their significance in biology generally. Their thermophilism has a bearing on the temperature relations, ecology, and evolution of other microorganisms. Their activities are of immediate concern in the great cycles of matter and energy that are the essence of biology. And their metabolism is intimately concerned in a number of highly practical phases of agriculture, industry, and medicine. We have attempted in the last part of our treatment, therefore, to review these interesting facets of thermophilism and place them in the broader perspective of biology, including its basic as well as its applied aspects.

We are glad to have this opportunity to express our appreciation to the many people who have helped us in our studies. Dr. C. B. van Niel and Dr. Paul J. Allen provided frequent stimulus and friendly encouragement throughout the first phase of the work at Salinas. Dr. Lee Bonar and Dr. W. C. Snyder advised us often on mycological questions. Dr. G. F. Papenfuss, Dr. J. Proskauer and Dr. Paul C. Silva have given generously of their special skill in the intricacies of taxonomy. Dr. L. C. Erickson cut the sections of cleistothecia and took the photographs for Plates 1–3. Mr. V. G. Duran aided us in preparing the final prints for these plates, and Mr. A. A. Blaker made the pictures for the two color plates. Mrs. Lois Taylor inked the drawings for Figures 10–20 and 62–64, and Dr. Sharon K. DeLong and Miss Charlotte Mentges prepared Figures 68–74. Several capable friends filled the broad chinks in our own limited linguistic abilities: Dr. Robert Ornduff, Mrs. E. Malofewoff, Mrs. Dolores Gerber, and Mr. Arthur Setteducati with the Russian; Mrs. Patricia Mascarenhas and Mrs. Enid M. Emerson with the Italian; and Dr. Rimo Bacigalupi with Latin as well as Italian. To all these kind people we are deeply grateful. We also take pleasure in thanking Dr. E. V. Crisan for making the work of his master's thesis fully available to us and for keeping us informed of his own very capable master's and doctor's research on the thermophilic fungi. On many occasions the funds allocated to the second author from the University of California, Berkeley, Committee on Research, provided support for essential aspects of our work and were deeply appreciated. We are indebted to Professors Robert M. Page of Stanford University and William C. Snyder of the University of California, Berkeley, who reviewed our manuscript. When all is said and done, however, ours is the full responsibility for what appears in this volume.

DONALD G. COONEY
RALPH EMERSON

February 1, 1964

CONTENTS

PART I

Background

1

INTRODUCTION: THERMOPHILIC FUNGI DEFINED

Temperature is undoubtedly the most important environmental variable affecting the
growth of bacteria.

JOHN L. INGRAHAM (1962, p. 265)

Whether temperature is the *most* important variable in the environment of living things some may debate, but none will doubt the cardinal role that temperature plays in the vital processes of all living things. Man has learned to modify the normal temperature extremes of his environment, and in all warm-blooded animals (homoiotherms) there has evolved a highly intricate mechanism for the control of body temperature within amazingly narrow limits. However, the vast majority of living things, including all lower animals and the whole plant kingdom as well as the entire array of microorganisms, can deviate little from the ambient temperatures of their environment.

Of this great assemblage of poikilothermic or heterothermic organisms, relatively very few will be found thriving at temperatures below 10°C or above 40°C. Those that grow and multiply vigorously outside this range may be spoken of as psychrophiles if they occur at low temperatures or thermophiles if they thrive at high temperatures. Both groups are of special interest to the biologist who considers the question: To what do these organisms owe their particular adaptation to unusually low or unusually high temperatures?

Thermophily—literally, a love of heat—is a characteristic that appears among widely different groups of organisms. Brues (1927) and Vouk (1950), among others, have summarized information regarding the occurrence of animals in hot springs. Crustacea, molluscs, and insects are reported at temperatures up to 50°C, and nematodes too may occur at temperatures as high as 50°C or possibly somewhat higher. Mitchell's (1960) interesting study of the evolution and ecology of thermophilic water mites has recently come to our attention. Whereas few if any higher plants can be considered truly thermophilic, among the thallophytes thermophily has been strongly developed. Best known to botanists are the thermophilic blue-green algae or Cyanophyceae, some of which thrive in hot springs at temperatures of 80–85°C * (compare Copeland, 1936). The thermophilic bacteria (Allen, 1953) and Actinomycetes (Henssen, 1957a) have also been the subject of intensive research. They are widespread, of great importance in many natural microbial processes, and of special interest to the microbiologist concerned with temperature adaptations. They are found growing where temperatures range up to 85°C * or possibly slightly higher. Gaughran (1947), Allen (1953), and other investigators have reviewed the early literature pertaining to these groups.

Besides the algae, bacteria, and Actinomycetes, there is another group of quite different microorganisms that display the property of thermophily, though to a less spectacular degree. They are members of the true fungi—Eumycetes or Eumycota—with temperature maxima between 50° and 60°C. Of these thermophilic fungi only six species had been described prior to our own studies, and they have remained about as little known to the average mycologist as they are to the general microbiologist or bacteriologist. Even though the first thermophilic true fungus, *Mucor pusillus*, was described about 75 years ago (Lindt, 1886), only the barest recognition of these specialized microorganisms has found its way into mycological or microbiological literature. Standard, current textbooks of mycology make little or no mention of them at all. One (Wolf and Wolf, 1947), which devotes a special chapter to effects of temperature on fungi, says absolutely nothing of thermophily. Three others (Hawker, 1950; Lilly and Barnett, 1951; Cochrane, 1958), which emphasize physiology and summarize extensive material on the temperature relations of fungi, present little accurate information on the thermophiles. Hawker ignores them except for a brief mention of *Chaetomium thermophile*. She cites species of *Sordaria* as examples of high-temperature organisms and gives temperatures of 40–45°C as the upper limits of growth, whereas at least five truly thermophilic molds, all capable of growing at temperatures above 50°C, had been described in detail before 1950. Lilly and Barnett also fail to include a discussion of any of the true thermophiles, listing only *Aspergillus fumigatus* and recording

---

* For recent evidence indicating maxima nearer to 75°C, see Kempner, E. S., 1963. Upper temperature limit of life. *Science,* **142:** 1318–1319.

45–50°C as its maximum temperature. Cochrane does devote a short para-graph to the thermophilic true fungi, even mentioning four of them by name and giving a few references to the literature. Several recent treatises and reviews covering temperature relations in microorganisms (for example, Gaughran, 1947; Precht et al., 1955) have included hardly anything on thermophilic fungi. Even Mishustin (1950), in his comprehensive volume *Thermophilic Microorganisms in Nature and Practice*, gives a very cursory and inadequate treatment of the true fungi.

Copeland (1936) includes in his bibliography the work of Tsiklinskaya (1899), who clearly demonstrated that the fungus *Thermomyces lanuginosus* grows at temperatures between 55° and 60°C. Yet he erroneously asserts (p. 210) that "The temperature limits of the other plant groups [that is, other than bacteria and blue-green algae] are in no case in excess of 51.0°C." Furthermore, Copeland (1936, p. 208) lists 37.2°C as the highest known temperature for Phycomycetes, despite the fact that Lindt (1886) and Miehe (1907a) had shown years before that certain species of *Mucor* thrive in the range 50–60°C.

In view of the intensive investigations that have been made of thermo-philic algae and bacteria, the lack of knowledge about thermophilic fungi is quite surprising. However, an examination of the literature clearly reveals the reason for this situation. Hitherto no mycologist has devoted himself to a study of this entire group of fungi (but see Cooney, 1952). What general and comparative knowledge we have of them has come to us largely from observations reported by investigators whose interest was more in the activi-ties of thermophilic microorganisms than in their detailed morphology or taxonomy. Thus Miehe (1907a, 1907b, 1930a, 1930b), to whom we owe most of the early information about the activities of thermophilic fungi, was par-ticularly concerned with the process of microbial thermogenesis in hay. He even expressed considerable lack of respect for some of the herbarium-type fungal taxonomy that characterized much mycological work of his time. Waksman and his colleagues (Waksman and Gerretsen, 1931; Waksman, Umbreit, and Cordon, 1939; Waksman and Cordon, 1939) focused their at-tention upon the microbial decomposition of plant residues in soils and com-posts and obviously had little detailed knowledge of the thermophilic true fungi they encountered, while the Russian workers (Isachenko and Mal'-chevskaya, 1936; Mal'chevskaya, 1939) were concerned more with the gen-eral microbiology and spontaneous heating of peat than with the classifica-tion or structure of the fungi they found. But, as we shall see, each of the strictly mycological studies that was made involved only one or occasionally two of the thermophilic fungi, and no comprehensive comparison and evaluation of all of them was ever prepared. That such a monographic treatment was urgently needed became apparent to us some twenty years ago when we made our first acquaintance with thermophilic fungi and their interesting activities.

Before embarking upon an account of our own observations, we shall present a brief summary of the earlier reports of thermophilic fungi. To do this in a sound fashion requires that we limit the area of discussion by defining what we mean by the term thermophile as applied to the true fungi. Much has been written and many arguments have been brought forth in defense of one or another person's definition of this and related terms as they apply to one or another group of organisms. The interested reader will find a scholarly summary and discussion of this matter in Crisan's (1959) master's thesis. Without laboring the question here we can recognize three points: (1) different organisms have very different cardinal temperatures—maximum, optimum, and minimum for growth; (2) if enough different organisms are considered, a complete cline or gradient of cardinal temperatures can be produced (see Vouk, 1950); hence (3) there is no a priori true definition of thermophile; what is reasonable for one group of organisms may be meaningless for another. Thus, for example, to the algologist a thermophile may have a maximum between 60° and 80°C, whereas to the bacteriologist it might have a slightly lower maximum, say 55° to 80°C, and the acarologist would have to place the limit much lower, say 35° to 45°C. If minimum or optimum temperatures are used instead, a similar situation pertains.

Most of the work on thermophiles has been done by bacteriologists, and their definition, although generally applicable to the bacteria, is quite inappropriate for the true fungi. To be meaningful and useful for the fungi our definition must be based upon our general experience of the temperature relations within the group. Most fungi grow between the limits of 10° and 40°C and have an optimum somewhere around 25–35°C (Cochrane, 1958). These can be thought of as mesophilic. But there are a few fungi that grow at temperatures above 50°C and still fewer that, besides being able to grow above 50°C, are unable to grow at ordinary laboratory temperatures—so-called "room temperature," approximately 20°C. Hence *our working definition of a thermophilic fungus is one that has a maximum temperature for growth at or above 50°C and a minimum temperature for growth at or above 20°C.* Fungi such as *Aspergillus fumigatus* or *Absidia ramosa*, with maxima near 50°C but minima well below 20°C, we consider to be *thermotolerant* and have arbitrarily excluded them from our treatment (see §13).

Crisan (1959), following a similar line of reasoning, defined thermophilic fungi as those whose optimum temperature for normal growth lies at or above 40°C. Such a definition is perfectly acceptable, but we find ours preferable because (1) end points (maxima and minima) are more readily established than optima; (2) agreement on whether a culture shows normal or abnormal growth is not always easy to reach; and (3) there are many fungi with optima above 40°C that still grow vigorously at temperatures well below 20°C. Indeed, according to his own definition, Crisan should probably have included in his account quite a number of additional species.

When the present study was begun, the literature available disclosed accounts of only six thermophilic molds satisfying our criteria of a minimum no lower than 20°C and a maximum no lower than 50°C. The earliest of these references relates to *Mucor pusillus*, a Phycomycete isolated and described by Lindt in 1886. This mold is generally considered the first of the known high-temperature fungi to be studied. In 1899 Tsiklinskaya described a Deuteromycete, capable of growing at high temperatures, which she named *Thermomyces lanuginosus*. Miehe (1907a, 1907b) described the third and fourth species of this group, to which he assigned the names *Thermoascus aurantiacus* and *Thermoidium sulfureum*. Following Miehe were Griffon and Maublanc, who in 1911 erected the thermophilic species *Penicillium duponti*. One year later Noack (1912) included the previously described *Anixia spadicea* in the thermophilic group.*

---

* The names of the above organisms are listed as given by the original authors. Subsequent changes, as well as recently proposed emendations, will be noted in the chapter in which each organism is discussed.

2

METHODS OF ISOLATION AND CULTURE

Natural Substrata

As we have noted in the Preface, all of our early isolates of thermophiles came from retted guayule shrub, so it will be well to say a few words here about how the rets were set up. The guayule plant, *Parthenium argentatum* Gray, is a rather woody perennial composite shrub. It was harvested from the field with roots cut about six inches below the crown. In the processing factory the whole plants were plunged into boiling water for ten minutes and then tumbled in a screen cage to remove the leaves. These defoliated plants were either baled and retted whole (bale ret) or put through a chopper equipped with screens to give particle sizes of one quarter inch up to one inch or more. The chopped shrub was adjusted to a moisture level between 35 and 50 percent and set to ret either in masses several feet deep in aerated bins (bin ret) or in masses about a foot deep spread on the floor (floor ret). Most of the thermophilic fungi from guayule were derived from stationary (unturned) bale, bin, or floor rets. Extensive and often rapid microbial decomposition took place in the rets, and because the material was quite effectively self-insulated, temperatures in the retting material soon reached 40–60°C and remained at these high levels for the major part of the retting period (Fig. 1). These, then, are the conditions that proved to be so favorable for the natural development of thermophilic fungi. Reference will be made in later sections to other aspects of guayule retting, and a full account of the process can be found in the report by Allen and Emerson (1949).

Our subsequent exploration for known thermophiles or possible new forms was guided by the high-temperature requirements of these fungi. As Miehe (1907a, 1907b), Griffon and Maublanc (1911), Noack (1912), and others had shown, and as our own detailed work on guayule had re-

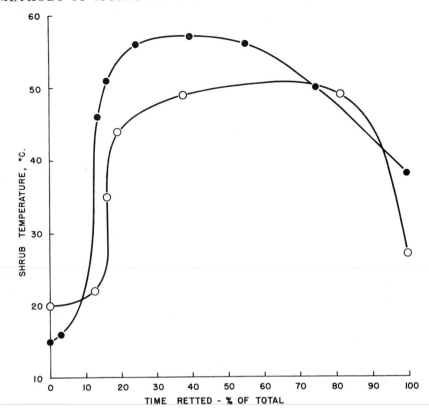

Fig. 1.

Time-course of typical self-heating (thermogenesis) of insulated, actively de-composing, damp plant materials. The total time of the decomposition and heating will depend, among other factors, upon the particle size of the material decomposing. Hence the longitudinal axis of the graph is shown as percent of the total time. Data for these curves were obtained from retting guayule in which material cut to about one-half inch would complete its rapid decomposition and heating in 5 to 8 days, whereas whole defoliated shrub retted in the bale might continue to heat for as long as 21 days or more. Similar curves for heating of damp hay (Hüni, 1954), compost (Golueke and Gotaas, 1954), or other material can be found in the literature.

vealed, thermophilic fungi were to be found in nature where organic materials were decomposing at elevated temperatures that usually resulted from microbial thermogenesis but sometimes depended upon insolation or the presence of warm-blooded animals. Accordingly, damp hay, leaf mold and other composting materials, straw, and dung of several herbivorous animals were the first materials collected for study. Soil samples from several widely separated localities, birds' nests, and wood-rats' nests were also investigated. Vegetable refuse in various stages of decomposition was obtained from the Sanitary Engineering Research Laboratory, University of California, where such material was being experimentally converted into humus. This too was thoroughly examined.

Preparation of Gross Cultures

Sometimes, as with many of the samples taken from guayule rets, thermophilic fungi were recognized right on the natural substratum and could be subcultured directly. Often, however, samples of the various organic substrata did not reveal any thermophilic forms until they had been incubated. For this purpose they were chopped into small pieces, well moistened, and placed in crystallizing dishes that had previously been lined with several thicknesses of moist paper toweling. The dishes were then covered with glass lids and incubated at 50°C for several days. Originally three incubators were used, with temperatures maintained at 30°, 40°, and 50°C, respectively. But it was soon found that at 30°C many ubiquitous saprophytic fungi appeared, and that even at 40°C some of these fungi were evident. Dishes held at 50°C, however, were noticeably free of true fungi except for thermophilic forms and one or two thermotolerant species. Thus, because of the suppression of nonthermophilic molds at the highest temperature level, we could be confident that those that did appear were very likely to be true thermophiles. The laborious process of isolating numerous molds from material held at 30° and 40°C, in the hope that some of these might prove to be thermophilic, was therefore discontinued. Crisan (1959) gives an interesting account of possible methods for collecting and isolating thermophilic fungi. He too found that he could obtain thermophiles with fewer contaminating fungi if he incubated his cultures at temperatures above 40°C. Temperatures of 45–50°C in essence provide an enrichment environment for thermophilic molds. Failure of previous investigators to provide this environment almost certainly accounts for our relatively sparse knowledge of thermophiles. Mycologists rarely incubate their cultures at temperatures above 20–23°C (room temperature). And what sensible mycologist would ever put his gross or pure cultures at 50°C?

After several days our gross cultures were examined with a high-power stereoscopic dissecting microscope. When known or possible thermophiles were found, the spores were transferred to agar plates by means of a sterile inoculating needle. If perithecia or cleistothecia were produced, transfers were made with sterile needle-tweezers (compare Emerson and Cantino, 1948). The agar plates were then incubated, and here again the temperature of incubation was critical. First attempts to grow some of the most prevalent and conspicuous thermophiles from guayule on agar met with repeated failure. This was not because the media were unsatisfactory but simply because the high-temperature requirement of these fungi was not recognized at first. All mold cultures at that time were routinely being held at room temperature or were occasionally placed in incubators at 30°C. At these temperatures the thermophiles grew very slightly or not at all and were promptly overgrown by mesophilic forms. When, however, spores of several species which had failed to grow at room temperature were held at 45° or 50°C, rapid germination and growth ensued. It soon became regular practice, therefore, to incubate primary transfer plates, just like gross cultures, at 50°C until good growth was established. Thereafter they could be removed to a 40°C incubator to prevent too rapid drying out of the agar.

Maintenance of adequate moisture in all cultures was a problem at the temperatures being used. Even a short exposure to 50°C resulted in drying out and splitting of the agar in the petri dishes. This condition was alleviated somewhat by placing the agar plates in large, glass moist-chambers lined with damp toweling. The paper was dampened only slightly, for excessively high humidities caused condensation and prevented normal development of the fungi.

The primary agar cultures thus obtained were obviously not always pure, but most were unifungal. *Aspergillus fumigatus* gave trouble on several occasions, but it was usually possible to avoid this mold if transfers of the desired fungi were made before the *Aspergillus* had formed and released its conidia. Thermophilic bacteria sometimes presented a more serious problem and necessitated final purification of several of the fungi by single-spore isolations. Crisan (1959) found antibiotics a ready means for keeping bacterial contamination at a low level.

Single-spore Isolations and Study of Pure Cultures

Single-spore cultures were prepared in a manner similar to that described by Bisby (1953). Two tubes of clear, sterile, melted YpSs agar (see p. 13) were prepared for each fungus to be isolated. After allowing the agar to cool slightly, spores were transferred from a gross culture to one of the agar tubes, which was then gently shaken. A loop of this suspension was then transferred to the second tube, and the contents of this tube were poured directly into a sterile, standard-size petri dish. The dish was quickly rotated, allowed to cool, and then placed in an inverted position in the incubator. Care was taken to select petri dishes with clear, unscratched bottoms, which facilitated observation of the germinating spores.

The dilution plates were at first incubated for twenty-four hours at 40°C. This proved to be far too long a time, for when the plates were examined the germinating spores had grown so rapidly that it was impossible to select individual sporelings. Because of this characteristic rapid growth of thermophilic fungi, single sporelings had to be isolated within twelve hours. The germlings were located by observing the inverted petri dishes under the low-power objective of the compound microscope. After the locations of suitable sporelings were marked by a small circle of India ink on the surface of the glass, the dishes were placed under the dissecting microscope and the germinating spores were removed by means of a flamed needle to sterile agar slants. These tubes were then incubated at 40°C until growth was complete. Transfers of these cultures were later made to agar plates, and it was these plate cultures which provided the material for study and descriptions. Morphological studies were usually made from material mounted on slides in lactophenol and cotton blue. Certain of the fungi, however—particularly those imperfect species which form chains of spores that are easily displaced when handled—did not lend themselves to this type of observation. Instead, if the dilution plates were incubated for several days until growth was abundant and were then examined directly under the low-power objective, such imperfect fungi could be studied without disrupting their growth pattern. Thus a truer picture of these organisms could be obtained than when conventional slide mounts were made.

Culture Media

Although nearly all of the thermophilic fungi appeared abundantly on natural substrata, it was not always easy to get them established on laboratory media. Several media were tried at first, some of which were unsatisfactory. A nutrient agar containing beef extract and peptone favored bacterial growth and was particularly subject to excessive desiccation at the high temperatures being used. Potato dextrose agar tended to shrivel along the surface at the higher temperatures and likewise proved unsatisfactory. The four standard media shown below were most useful, and of these yeast-starch agar (YpSs) and yeast-glucose agar (YG) were particularly favorable. A few other media were employed for special purposes, and their composition will be indicated at the appropriate point in the discussion.

YpSs: Yeast-Starch agar (Emerson, 1941)

Difco powdered yeast extract	4.0 g
K_2HPO_4	1.0 g
$MgSO_4 \cdot 7H_2O$	0.5 g
Soluble Starch	15.0 g
Agar	20.0 g
Water ($\frac{1}{4}$ tap, $\frac{3}{4}$ distilled)	1000 ml

YG: Yeast-glucose agar

Difco powdered yeast extract	5.0 g
Glucose	10.0 g
Agar	20.0 g
Tap water	1000 ml

OA: Oatmeal agar (Emerson, 1941)

Oatmeal	50.0 g
(in 700 ml tap water, steamed for one hour and strained through muslin)	
Agar	20.0 g
Tap water	to make 1000 ml

C3: Czapek's agar (Raper and Thom, 1949)

$NaNO_3$	3.0 g
K_2HPO_4	1.0 g
$MgSO_4 \cdot 7H_2O$	0.5 g
KCL	0.5 g
$FeSO_4 \cdot 7H_2O$	0.01 g
Sucrose	30.0 g
Agar	20.0 g
Tap water	to make 1000 ml

General Practices

Standard sterile procedures were followed throughout in the preparation of agar plates and slants and in the transferring of cultures. Agar media, either in test tubes or stock flasks, were autoclaved for twenty minutes at 15 pounds pressure. Small petri dishes (6-cm diameter) were generally used for plate cultures. The line drawings were all made with the aid of a camera lucida.

PART II

The Species of Thermophilic Fungi: Culture, Development, Morphology, and Systematics

3

MUCOR PUSILLUS AND MUCOR MIEHEI

Mucor Micheli (1729, p. 215) ex Fries (1832, p. 317)

Mucor pusillus Lindt (1886, pp. 272–275)
SYN.: *Mucor buntingii* Lendner (1929, p. 260)
   Mucor hagemii Naumov (1935, p. 55)*

Mucor miehei n. sp.

Although the organism designated in the literature as *Mucor pusillus* has in the past been repeatedly isolated and studied in detail, and although different investigators agree with one another on most points of comparison, when different descriptions of *M. pusillus* are examined it is obvious that discrepancies exist. The reasons for such discrepancies became clear as a result of our extensive study of several thermophilic isolates of the genus *Mucor*, for this study has led us to conclude that there exist not one but two distinct thermophilic species of *Mucor*. One of these species is clearly *M. pusillus* Lindt, for our isolates agree in every respect with the original description of this organism by Lindt. The other species, although similar to *M. pusillus*, is different in certain respects, particularly in the method of zygospore production. This organism we are proposing as the new species *Mucor miehei*.

Occurrence of the Two Species

Lindt (1886) first described *Mucor pusillus* growing on bread, and several investigators have subsequently isolated thermophilic *Mucors* from a variety

---

* It is possible that the name *M. hagemii* was used earlier than this by Naumov, because the present citation is to Naumov's second edition. We have been unable, however, to establish what Naumov considered to be the first edition, and so we have not succeeded in determining whether or not there is an earlier date.

of substrata. Miehe (1907a) observed a thermophilic *Mucor* in self-heated hay, and although he assumed his organism was identical to *M. pusillus* Lindt, we have concluded, for reasons discussed later, that Miehe's organism was actually a new species. Hagem (1908) isolated *M. pusillus*, this time directly from the air, and Noack (1912), in his study of thermophilic organisms, also isolated what he considered to be a strain of *M. pusillus*. Several investigators have reported *M. pusillus*, and in at least one instance *M. miehei*, as a causative agent of animal mycoses. These records are discussed in more detail in §15. Zycha (1935) lists the two organisms *Mucor cornealis* Cavara and Saccardo (Saccardo, 1913) and *Mucor buntingii* Lendner (1929) as synonyms under *M. pusillus* Lindt. We believe, however, that only one of these isolates—*M. buntingii* Lendner—is acceptable as a synonym for *M. pusillus* (see p. 24). Lendner's organism, then, which he obtained from fermenting cacao seeds, represents a later isolate of *M. pusillus* made prior to our own study of this organism. Although most of the isolates of thermophilic *Mucors* have been described as lacking a zygosporic stage, a few instances have been recorded, aside from our own studies, in which zygospores have been observed (Miehe, 1907a; Noack, 1912; Smith, 1957; and Crisan, 1959). Although Miehe, Noack, and Smith have considered the observed zygospores to represent the sexual stage of *M. pusillus*, our own studies of several strains of thermophilic *Mucors* lead us to conclude that the zygosporic *Mucor* is a separate species from *M. pusillus*. Our isolates of the two species were obtained from different substrata collected from several localities.

The first isolate of *M. pusillus* (strain #9) investigated during this study was made by C. B. van Niel in 1944 from a standing (that is, unturned) guayule shrub ret. A second isolate (strain #D50-2) was obtained by Emerson in 1945 from retting guayule also, but in this case the chopped shrub was aerated in revolving drums with the temperature held close to 50°C. A third isolate (strain #M9) occurred on a gas mask stored in a tropical room at the Massachusetts Institute of Technology, and a culture of this organism was sent to Emerson in 1945 by V. M. Cutter. The fourth isolate studied (strain #M10) was sent to Emerson in 1946 by D. H. Linder, from the Blakeslee Collection at the Farlow Herbarium. In 1950 Cooney isolated the last two strains involved in this study. The first of these (strain #6) was obtained from leaf mold collected near Berkeley, California, which had been incubated at 50°C for four days; the second isolate (strain #8) occurred on incubated horse dung collected at Pyramid Lake, Nevada.

The original strain of *M. miehei* (strain #21) was isolated in 1944, also by van Niel, from aerated, retting guayule shrub. Subcultures of this isolate were subsequently used as the basis for the description and line drawings of *M. miehei*. In 1944 Emerson isolated another strain (strain #21A) from aerated guayule, and in 1945 still another isolate (strain #21B) was obtained by Emerson from a floor ret of guayule shrub. The last of the isolates (strain #35) of *M. miehei* to be studied was obtained by Cooney in 1950 from incubating horse dung collected near Reno, Nevada.

The Presence or Absence of Zygospores

Lindt (1886) first described the fungus *M. pusillus* in detail, and in addition determined the temperature limits of his new organism (see Table 2, p. 25). Details of the sporangia, spores, and mycelium are given by Lindt, but no zygospores were ever observed. Miehe (1907a), in his treatment of the organisms found occurring in moist hay, discusses a *Mucor* which was very common and which Miehe decided was the fungus previously described by Lindt. From the descriptions of the above two molds it is apparent that they are very similar morphologically. But Miehe, in contrast to Lindt, found that his organism commonly produced zygospores. These zygospores, according to Miehe, represented the previously unknown sexual stage of *M. pusillus*.

It is this apparent lack of zygospores in *M. pusillus* Lindt, and their presence in the *Mucor* studied by Miehe, which has, in part, led us to believe that the above workers were dealing with two distinct species of *Mucor*. One is *M. pusillus* Lindt and the other we propose here as a new species, *M. miehei*. Evidence for this conclusion comes from our detailed comparison of the several strains of thermophilic *Mucor* that we have isolated from retting guayule and obtained from other sources. The isolates of *M. miehei* regularly form large numbers of zygospores in single-spore cultures in three to five days on YpSs agar at 30–40°C. Indeed, the homothallic nature of this species was well established by five successive single-spore transfers of our isolate #21, through each of which the organism continued to form zygospores as copiously as ever, over the whole culture. These zygospores range from 30 to 50 μ (Fig. 8), or only slightly smaller than those reported by Miehe to be 40–50 μ. In addition to the normal zygospores, the presence of azygospores has been reported in cultures of *M. miehei* by Crisan (1959). He observed that gametangia may develop parthenogenetically, without benefit of sexual fusion, into what appear to be mature zygospores. Crisan further observed that although the gametangia may begin parthenogenetic development, their ability to undergo sexual fusion is not immediately lost, so that maturing gametangia of unequal, as well as equal, age may undergo sexual fusion.

Isolates of *M. pusillus*, on the contrary, have never been seen to form zygospores in single-spore cultures. When, however, our six isolates were crossed in various combinations, on YpSs agar at 40°C, they proved to represent two mating types, as shown in Table 1, and after three days numerous zygospores of this long-known species were obtained for the first time.

TABLE 1. Zygospore Production Resulting from Crossing Strains of *Mucor pusillus* Lindt.

Strain	#6	#M9	#M10	#8	#9	#D50-2
#6	—	—	—	++++	++++	++++
#M9	—	—	—	++	—	—
#M10	—	—	—	++	++	++
#8	++++	++	++	—	—	—
#9	++++	—	++	—	—	—
#D50-2	++++	—	++	—	—	—

The data presented in Table 1 indicate clearly that *M. pusillus* is a heterothallic species and that the production of zygospores is dependent upon the interaction of two compatible mycelia. However, the sexual reaction is much more pronounced in some matings (as with #6 × #8), where a distinct line of zygotes was formed along the line of contact between the two mycelia, than in others (as with #M10 × #8), where few zygospores were produced. Strain #M9 was so weak that it formed zygotes with only one of the strains of opposite mating type. Hence there appear to be marked differences in the sexual potency of various strains. It is not clear at present just how the differences are to be explained. Lindt's failure to observe zygospores in his original material, and the similar failure of subsequent investigators, can undoubtedly be ascribed to the existence of a heterothallic condition in *M. pusillus*. Our own observations regarding the heterothallic nature of *M. pusillus* have been substantiated, in part, by Crisan (1959), who crossed three of our isolates (#6, #8, and #9) and two of his strains (5–2B and IMUR 579) in various combinations. Crisan found, as we did, that some of the strains were apparently of the same mating type and hence produced no zygospores when crossed. In other crosses, however, certain strains mated readily, with zygospores produced as a consequence.

It seems appropriate at this point to comment on the recent work of Ainsworth and Austwick (1955) and of Smith (1957). In 1955 Ainsworth and Austwick obtained an isolate—presumably of *M. pusillus*—associated with mastitis in cattle, and another similar isolate from the brain and other organs of a calf. All of the isolates grew well at 37°C but died out when maintained at 25°C; probably, therefore, these isolates were true thermophiles. Two subsequent isolates were made from bovine female reproductive tracts. One zygosporic culture obtained from the above material was subsequently studied by Smith (1957), who decided that the fungus was homothallic. Colonies produced from single spores, as well as from single sporangiophores, produced zygospores freely. These zygospores, according to Smith, represent the sexual stage of *Mucor pusillus*. From the description of the organism investigated by Smith, it appears that very probably he, as Miehe apparently had done many years before, was dealing with the homothallic *Mucor miehei*, since the general description as indicated by Smith fits this fungus as well as *M. pusillus*. Furthermore, as we have demonstrated above, *M. pusillus* is heterothallic and zygospores are never formed from single-spore colonies.

Other Morphological Differences

Besides the important difference indicated above, the two species *M. pusillus* and *M. miehei* manifest contrasting details of less importance. *M. pusillus* produces a deeper turf of a neutral gray or hair brown (Ridgway); *M. miehei* is mouse gray in color and the colony is much more compact. Although the general size and shape of the sporangia, columellae, and sporangiospores are about the same for both species (Figs. 2–3 and 6–7), there is a noticeable difference in the appearance of the sporangiophore branching. Generally, in *M. pusillus* (Fig. 4), a group of sporangia develop on short branches at the tip of the main sporangiophore; *M. miehei* shows a looser, sympodial type of branching, with the lateral branches relatively longer (Fig. 9). Zygospores of *M. pusillus* are generally somewhat larger than those of *M. miehei*.

Taxonomy

A critical comparison of our isolates of the heterothallic species discussed above with Lindt's description of *M. pusillus* has convinced us that these two organisms are identical. We also believe that the homothallic species, *M. miehei*, is the same organism discussed by Miehe in 1907, but which Miehe failed to recognize as another species of *Mucor*. Apparently Miehe

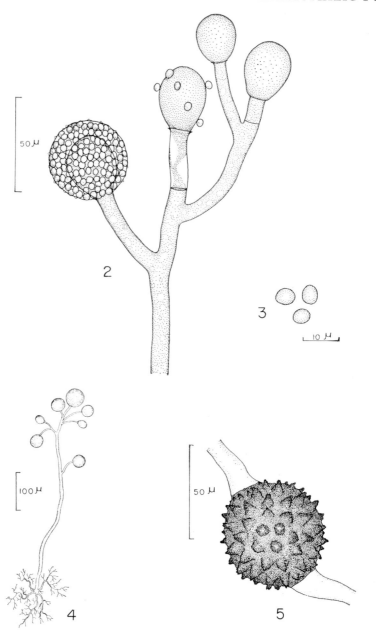

Figs. 2–5. *Mucor pusillus.*
  Fig. 2. Apical portion of a sporangiophore bearing a mature sporangium; to the right are columellae of dehisced sporangia. Fig. 3. Sporangiospores. Fig. 4. Sporangiophore which has developed directly from a single spore; note general distribution of sporangia near tip portion. Fig. 5. Mature zygospore.

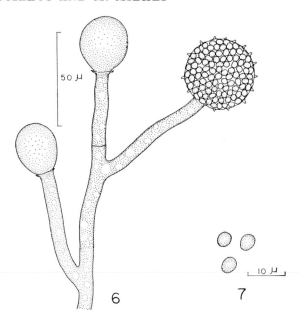

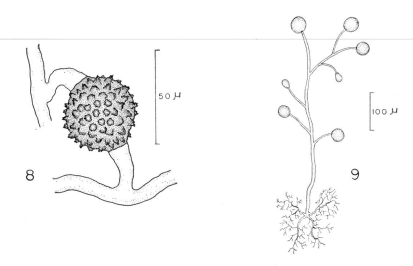

Figs. 6–9. *Mucor miehei.*
    Fig. 6. Terminal portion of a sporangiophore showing a sporangium and two columellae. Fig. 7. Sporangiospores. Fig. 8. Mature zygospore. Fig. 9. Sporangiophore which has developed from a single spore.

did not attach much importance to the presence of zygospores in his species and the complete lack of these structures in *M. pusillus*. That Miehe's interest was more in the phenomenon of thermophilism itself than in mycology may explain his apparent unawareness of the implications of Blakeslee's (1904) discovery of heterothallism in the *Mucorales*.

From our conviction of the distinctness of *M. miehei*, it seemed that this fungus should unquestionably be described as a new species of *Mucor*. Complications arose, however, when a review of the literature revealed that Kanouse (1923) isolated and described a homothallic species of *Mucor* (*M. parvispora*), with which *M. miehei* agrees on several important points. In other respects, however, the two fungi are quite dissimilar. There is, first of all, a decided difference in the height of the turf produced. Whereas Kanouse indicates the depth of the colony of *M. parvispora* as being less than three centimeters, we have observed the turf of our isolates to be extremely short—at most only a few millimeters tall. Differences in the color of the mature zygospores are also evident. And the spiny nature of the sporangial wall of *M. miehei* is in contrast to the smooth wall reported for the sporangia of *M. parvispora*. Furthermore, although Kanouse observed the presence of chlamydospores and oidiospores in her cultures, Miehe did not, nor have we seen these spore forms in any of the isolates studied.

The main discrepancy between the two fungi involves the temperature requirements for growth. Kanouse states that her species was described from cultures grown on fresh white bread, at a temperature of 25°C. She makes no mention of the possibility that her fungus might grow at elevated temperatures. We have found, on the other hand, that our isolates grow very slowly at 25°C, even on moist white bread, but at temperatures of 35–50°C, on the same substratum, growth is very rapid.

Table 2 presents some of the outstanding comparative characteristics of the three species of *Mucor* discussed in the present report. The several morphological differences (along with obvious physiological differences concerning temperature requirements for growth) listed in the table, as well as in the foregoing text, are sufficient evidence in our opinion to conclude that the three species of *Mucor* in question are distinct species. Therefore, the name *Mucor miehei* is proposed for the new thermophilic species typified by our strain #21, isolated from retting guayule shrub.

As indicated earlier, Zycha (1935) includes *Mucor cornealis* Cavara and Saccardo and *M. buntingii* Lendner as synonyms under *M. pusillus* Lindt. Although Naumov (1935, p. 55) lists the organism *M. buntingii* Lendner as a distinct species, we have concluded, after comparing the description of

TABLE 2. Comparative Characteristics of *Mucor pusillus, M. miehei,* and *M. parvispora.*

Characteristic	M. pusillus Lindt	M. miehei n. sp.	M. parvispora Kanouse
Colony color	White to pallid neutral or deep neutral gray to hair brown (Ridgway)	White to mouse gray or dark mouse gray to dark Quaker drab (Ridgway)	White to drab or smoky gray (Ridgway)
Depth of colony	Turf thick, up to 2–3 mm	Turf thin, up to 2 mm	Turf very thick, but less than 30 mm high
Sporangiophores	Branched, mostly sympodially, colorless, older yellow-brown	Branched, mostly sympodially, colorless	Branched sympodially, colorless
Sporangia	Spherical, 50–80 μ, wall with short spines	Spherical, 30–60 μ, wall with short spines	Spherical, 30–52 μ, wall smooth
Zygospores	None except in cross. Subspherical, tuberculate, reddish brown to black, 45–63 μ	Numerous, sub-spherical, tuberculate, reddish brown to black, 30–50 μ	Spherical, tuberculate, golden brown, 20–65 μ
Sexuality	Heterothallic	Homothallic	Homothallic
Temperature limits	20–55°C; growth slow at 20–30°C	25–57°C; growth extremely slow at 25–30°C	Not given; grown only at 25°C

this organism with the characteristics of our own isolates of *M. pusillus* and with the original description of *M. pusillus* given by Lindt, that *M. buntingii* Lendner should be retained as a synonym under *M. pusillus* Lindt, as proposed by Zycha. On the other hand, it is our opinion that Zycha was in error in including *M. cornealis* Cavara and Saccardo (Saccardo, 1913) as a synonym for *M. pusillus* Lindt. We believe that two important characteristics of *M. cornealis* preclude the possibility that these two organisms are identical. The first of these characters concerns the general morphology of the sporangium and columella. Cavara's paper (1913, Fig. III) clearly shows that the sporangium of *M. cornealis* is distinctly apophysate, a characteristic typical of *Absidia* rather than of *Mucor*. The second character involves the temperature limits that Cavara lists for growth of *M. cornealis*. He says that the temperature range within which his organism will grow is from 15° to 51° or 52°C. The temperature range for our isolates of M pusillus is from 20° to 55°C. Our figures agree closely with the figures given by Lindt (1886) in his original description of M. pusillus.

If M. cornealis Cavara and Saccardo is to be removed as a synonym for M. pusillus Lindt, as we have proposed above, then Absidia cornealis (V. Cavara and Saccardo) Dodge, n. comb., and Lichtheimia cornealis (Cavara and Saccardo) Naumov must also be deleted. These two names have also been listed as synonyms for M. pusillus (compare Crisan, 1959). But Dodge (1935, p. 114) lists M. cornealis under the former name (Absidia cornealis), and Naumov (1935, p. 77) places M. cornealis in synonymy under the name Lichtheimia cornealis. All three names obviously apply to one and the same organism.

One final taxonomic point we wish to make clear concerns our placing of Mucor hagemii Naumov in synonymy with M. pusillus Lindt. From Hagem's (1908) description of his organism, it is evident that he had an isolate of M. pusillus—the morphological characters of his organism, including the absence of zygospores, agree in every respect with our observations on this fungus. That his cultures did not grow below 30°C but did grow well at 31–40°C also leads us to conclude that he had the thermophilic M. pusillus.

Diagnoses

Mucor pusillus Lindt

Turf 2–3 mm high, at first white, later deep neutral gray to hair brown; sporangiophores 10 μ in diameter, branched sympodially, colorless at first, later yellow-brown; sporangia spherical, 50–80 μ in diameter, wall beset with short spines; columellae subspherical to slightly elongate, 15–35 μ in diameter, often up to 60 μ in length, provided with a collar; sporangiospores colorless, spherical to subglobose, 3–5 μ in diameter; zygospores present only in crosses of two compatible mycelia, subspherical, warty, reddish brown when young, black at maturity, 45–63 μ in diameter.

Mucor pusillus is represented by specimens M206520 (our culture #6) and M206521 (our culture #8) in the University of California Herbarium, Berkeley.

Mucor miehei n. sp.

Turf short, 1–2 mm high, at first white, later mouse gray; sporangiophores 8 μ in diameter, branched sympodially; sporangia spherical, 30–60 μ in diameter, walls beset with short spines; columellae spherical to oval, 20–45 μ in diameter; sporangiospores colorless, subspherical to oval, 4–6 × 3–5 μ; zygospores numerous, subspherical, warty, yellowish to reddish brown when young, blackish when mature, 30–50 μ in diameter, produced on a homothallic mycelium; azygospores present in some strains; gemmae unknown.

HABITAT: On retting guayule shrub.

Mucor miehei sp. nov., caespite breve alto 1–2 mm, primo acolorato demum colore murino, sporangiophoricus diametro 8 μ ramosis sympodice sporangiis globosis diametro 30–60 μ, parietibus circumdatis spinis brevibus, columellis globosis vel ovalibus diametro 20–45 μ, sporangiosporis hyalinis subglobosis vel ovalibus 4–6 × 3–5 μ, zygosporis numerosis subglobosis diametro 30–50 μ, verrucis subnigris ad maturitatem, azygosporis praesentes in aliquibus generibus, gemmis incognitis. In frutice putrescente guayule dicto habitat.

Mucor miehei is represented by specimen M206519 (our culture #21).

Temperature Relations

Mucor pusillus and *M. miehei* exhibit a marked difference in the rate of growth at the lower temperature limits. While *M. pusillus* grows slowly at 20°C and more rapidly at 30°C, *M. miehei* grows extremely slowly at 25°C and still rather slowly at 30°C. Most rapid growth of both organisms occurs within the range of 35–45°C. Heavy colonies bearing numerous sporangia were produced by both fungi at 50°C, but at 55°C only sterile mycelia were produced. *M. pusillus* grew very poorly at 55°C and showed no growth at 57°C, whereas *M. miehei* produced slight growth at 57°C.

4

TALAROMYCES (PENICILLIUM) DUPONTI

Talaromyces Benjamin (1955, p. 681)

and *Penicillium* Link ex Fries (1832, pp. 406–407)

> ***Talaromyces** (Penicillium) duponti* (**Griffon and Maublanc,** 1911; **emend. Emerson,** in Raper and Thom, 1949, pp. 573–577). **Apinis** (1963a)
>
> IMPERFECT STAGE: *Penicillium duponti* Griffon and Maublanc (1911)
> PROBABLE SYN.: *Citromyces sphagnicola* Mal'chevskaya (1939, p. 23)

Seldom reported and rarely studied is a thermophilic member of the Eurotiales, *Penicillium duponti*. It was named after Monsieur Dupont, who first discovered it in France and isolated it from manure and damp hay (see Griffon and Maublanc, 1911). The organism was then accurately described by Griffon and Maublanc, who correctly placed it in *Penicillium* and recognized its thermophilic character. They observed only the typical, asexual, conidial, reproductive phase at that time.

Interestingly enough, this fungus escaped the keen eye of Miehe (1907a) during his exhaustive studies on the microbial flora of self-heating hay. Moreover, to the best of our knowledge, it was not identified again until Emerson found it on retted guayule shrub in 1945. During the course of the cultural studies made in 1945, the perfect stage was discovered for the first time and recorded in detail. Subsequently, at the request of Dr. Kenneth B. Raper, a full account of this work, with drawings and photographs, was provided for inclusion in the monumental volume on *Penicillium* then being prepared by Raper and Thom (1949, pp. 573–577). In order to cover *P.*

duponti fully in the present account, we are reporting here again our original observations and providing the supporting illustrative material.

Occurrence

It is noteworthy that in most instances thus far *P. duponti* has been found when previously naturally heated materials were incubated in the laboratory at temperatures between 45° and 55°C. The first isolations were made by Dupont in connection with studies being carried out at the École Nationale d'Agriculture de Grignon. Although, as indicated by Griffon and Maublanc (1911), one isolate was obtained directly from fresh, slightly alkaline, naturally heated manure, the other came from moist hay that was incubated at 50°C. Possibly the fungus isolated from spontaneously heated peat that Mal'chevskaya reported in 1939 as *Citromyces sphagnicola* is referable to *Penicillium duponti* (see Taxonomy, p. 35). Our own two initial collections were derived from self-heated guayule shrub at Salinas, California. In the first instance (May, 1945), defoliated shrub, chopped to ½-inch size and raised to 50 percent moisture, was spread on the floor in a layer ten inches deep and retted for three days. The material was turned and mixed every six hours during the retting period, and it heated vigorously to temperatures of 50° to 56°C between turnings on the second and third days. Some of this material was removed and placed in an incubator for several days at 52°C—not 45°C, the temperature incorrectly reported to Raper and Thom and given by them (1949, p. 577). The fungal growth that appeared was mostly *Humicola lanuginosa*, but scattered patches of very delicate white mycelium proved to be *P. duponti*. In the second instance (December, 1945), the guayule was chopped to ½-inch size, adjusted to 35 percent moisture, and retted in a continuously rotating aerated drum at approximately 47°C for four days. The moisture was held at 30–35 percent by periodic addition of water, shrub temperature was held between 46° and 50°C by means of a water bath, and when a sample of shrub was taken on the fourth day the *p*H was 7.7. Portions of this sample, held for three additional days in an incubator at 47°C, once more revealed *P. duponti*.

When we made collections again some years later and incubated the materials, the fungus was isolated from several other plant substrata—composting leaf mold gathered near Reno, Nevada, damp straw from San Francisco, California, and leaf litter from Colfax, California. More recently,

Crisan (1959) failed to find it in his wide array of collections made in Pennsylvania and Indiana.

The general failure of earlier workers to recognize *Penicillium duponti* directly on naturally heated materials may be accounted for by its delicate structure, by its less vigorous growth—it would tend to be crowded out by such strong and common species as *Humicola lanuginosa*—by its lack of any bright pigmentation, and by its tendency to produce abundant cleistothecia only under rather special conditions. However, when enriched by incubation of appropriate substrata at elevated temperatures in the laboratory, *P. duponti* has frequently made its appearance in our own cultures and will probably prove to be one of the relatively ubiquitous and common thermophilic fungi.

Morphology and Cultural Characteristics

A concise account of this species, permitting ready comparison with other penicillia, appears in Raper and Thom (1949). The careful original description of the imperfect stage, provided by Griffon and Maublanc in 1911, fits our isolates with remarkable closeness. The several media used in our own investigations of *P. duponti*, besides chopped guayule shrub, were YG agar (on which our first isolations were made), OA agar, and C3 agar. Certain characteristics of the fungus were quite markedly affected by the cultural conditions, as will be noted.

Whether on chopped plant materials or in agar culture, the mycelium is composed of very delicate branched hyphae, mostly 2 to 2.5 or 3 μ in diameter, within the substratum or trailing over the surface. On YG agar the growth is fairly rapid at optimum temperatures of 45–50°C and can reach a diameter of about 8 cm in seven days. Raper and Thom (1949) report somewhat slower growth—about 5 cm in ten or twelve days—on C3 agar. The mycelium can be described as delicately floccose, becoming somewhat mealy in older cultures, 1 mm deep or less, and in age developing deeper tufts as overgrowths. Dark brown drops of liquid exudate are sometimes formed in the central areas of agar cultures. The growth is always white at the start and then generally develops some rather dull shade of grayish green, lavender, or pinkish brown. However, these delicate colors vary considerably, depending upon temperature, age, and substratum. Some typical examples are as follows. On YG agar at 35°C (see facing plate), there is a pale salmon-colored central area, with peripheral portions bluish green and a narrow (1 mm) white zone at the extreme front;

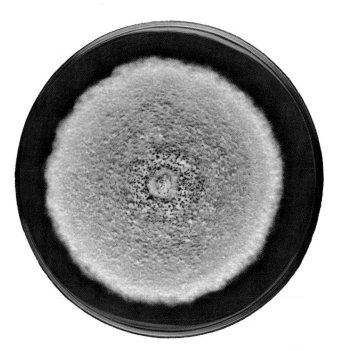

Talaromyces (*Penicillium*) *duponti*, 5 days at 45 °C
on yeast-glucose (YG) agar.

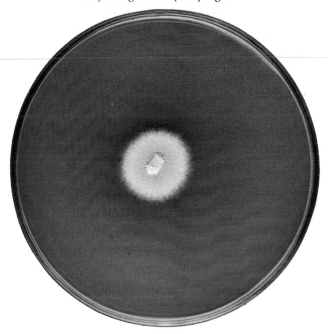

Talaromyces (*Penicillium*) *duponti*, 5 days at 35 °C
on yeast-glucose (YG) agar.

the underside (reverse) is pale salmon to greenish black. On YG agar, at temperatures above 40°C (see color plate), the growth is quite uniformly cinnamon-lavender to pale gray-rose; the reverse and agar are pinkish lavender to reddish brown. On C3 agar, the color is quite uniform regardless of temperature, remaining white for longer, then becoming very pale lavender, cinnamon-pink, or avellaneous; the reverse and agar are colorless or tinged with pale lavender. On OA agar at 37°C, the color is greenish gray, becoming pale lavender or avellaneous; the reverse and agar are pinkish brown. On chopped guayule shrub, the growth is first white, delicate, and cottony; then, with the start of conidium formation, it becomes pale gray to yellowish green, and finally dark mouse gray with greenish cast; white knots of hyphae become very conspicuous in four or five days at optimum temperatures and later develop into pale gray cleistothecia (see below). In summary, the lavender-avellaneous tones of a mature growth of *P. duponti* will usually serve to distinguish it from many of the common penicillia with their distinctly greenish color shades.

Conidiophores (Figs. 10 and 11) develop quite early on most media, usually as short lateral branches more or less perpendicular to the main hyphae from which they arise. They are often simple but not infrequently show 2, 3, or 4 irregular branches. They are smooth, 0- to 2-septate, 5–30 μ long and 2–3 μ in diameter, and generally slightly larger at the apex than the base. The penicilli themselves are small and very irregular, varying from monoverticillate, with 1 to 4 phialides at the apex of a short conidiophore, to partially or fairly regularly biverticillate. The few metulae that occur in a verticil are 5–7 × 2–3 μ. The sterigmata or phialides are divergent and 8–10 × 2 μ. Conidia are borne in long tangled chains that separate readily from the phialides. Disjunctors are not formed, and the conidia when mature are very pale yellow, smooth, generally elliptical or slightly ovoid, and 2–4.5 × 1.5–3 μ.

The perfect stage of *P. duponti* does not ordinarily occur on agar cultures and apparently requires some rather special conditions for its initiation. This matter will be discussed later, but we will note here that cleistothecia are formed regularly and abundantly on moist, chopped guayule shrub in small pure-culture rets. After four or five days at 45°C, they appear first as conspicuous white, cottony knots in the mycelium. By the seventh day they have become discrete little globose bodies, pearl gray, delicately leathery in texture, soft and pliable, and are attached to bits of shrub and the sides of the culture flasks by fine hyphae. At this stage it is already apparent that the external surface is composed of delicate, interwoven hyphae, and in the center of each young cleistothecium developing asci can be detected. In

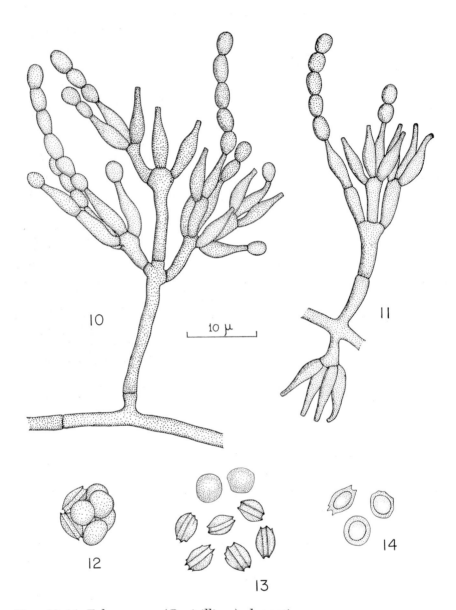

Figs. 10–14. *Talaromyces (Penicillium) duponti.*
Figs. 10 and 11. Conidiophores with penicilli, showing the types of irregularities that occur. Fig. 12. A cluster of eight ascospores as they were formed in the ascus; the evanescent ascus wall has already disintegrated. Fig. 13. Ascospores in surface view, showing equatorial furrow and ridges. Fig. 14. Ascospores in optical section, to show the thickened wall.

cultures that are 14 days old, numerous fully mature ascocarps occur (Plate 1). They are pale grayish tan, subspherical, scattered or irregularly clustered but usually not confluent, and 0.4 to 1.3 mm in diameter. The peridium is a distinct, smooth, papery layer that ruptures fairly cleanly under pressure but never shows an ostiolar opening. Microscopically it is revealed as a prosenchymatous covering (Plate 2). The outer hyphal elements are small and compact, whereas those toward the inside are larger (up to 10 μ in diameter), less compact, and nearly pseudoparenchymatous. The asci within are very numerous, scattered irregularly, subglobose, 9–10 μ in diameter, and 8-spored (Fig. 12). They disintegrate before the spores are mature. Ascospores (Figs. 13 and 14) are distinctively pale orange or tan in mass and very pale yellow when viewed singly by transmitted light. They are 3.5–5.0 × 2.5–3.5 μ and thick-walled. Like those of many other eurotialean species, they are generally lenticular and with a fairly well defined equatorial furrow flanked by low, smooth or somewhat jagged ridges. The convex surfaces are smooth or show occasional ridges and irregularities.

Ascospores were found to be mature in cultures ten to fourteen days old at 45°C. When such spores were plated on YG agar at 45°C, they germinated without special treatment, the two valves of the wall often separating as the germ tube emerged. Cultures derived from ascospores again gave the typical conidial stage of *P. duponti*, so the genetic relation between the perfect and imperfect phases was clearly established. Furthermore, single-ascospore cultures have again given rise to ascocarps, thus revealing that homothallism is characteristic of this species, as it apparently is in all other members of the Eurotiaceae.

Some information has been obtained regarding the conditions that initiate the ascosporic phase. Cleistothecia appear very rarely in ordinary agar cultures. They occurred only once on OA agar in a culture incubated at 40°C and were never found on numerous YG cultures in air. As already noted, however, they were formed profusely in cultures grown on chopped guayule shrub, and it was early observed that they appeared in greatest numbers on the bottoms of the culture flasks, underneath the substratum. On the hypothesis that a reduced level of oxygen was initiating ascocarp formation in the bottom of these shrub cultures, YG agar slants in test tubes were inoculated and grown for one week at 45°C in the usual way in air. Cultures were then placed in two jars, one of which was flushed for several hours with nitrogen gas while the other was similarly flushed with carbon dioxide. The jars were then sealed and returned to the 45°C incubator. A week later, the material treated with carbon dioxide looked bleached and moribund and showed no cleistothecia. The nitrogen-treated cultures, how-

ever, showed numerous cleistothecia scattered over the surface. Microscopic examination two weeks thereafter revealed fully formed, orange-colored ascospores in these cleistothecia. Crude as this preliminary experiment is, it suggests that alteration of the normal respiratory processes may in some way initiate sexual reproduction in *P. duponti*. The level of carbon dioxide is known to affect the reproductive process of other fungi (Emerson and Cantino, 1948; Cantino, 1956) and to have profound effects on the initiation of sexual activity in *Hydra* (Loomis, 1957). Should it be established that levels of oxygen or carbon dioxide do in fact play a determinative role in the initiation of ascocarps in *P. duponti*, an extensive series of tests on the species of imperfect penicillia and other Aspergillaceae would certainly be called for.

Taxonomy

Because it was correctly placed as to genus when first described by Griffon and Maublanc in 1911, and because it has been seen so seldom since then, little synonymy or other nomenclatural confusion has clouded the situation of *Penicillium duponti*. Unfortunately now, however, with recognition of its perfect stage, this fungus must become part of the general argument regarding the naming of perfect penicillia and aspergilli. If we follow Raper and Thom (1949) or Alexopoulos (1952), we will continue to call it *Penicillium duponti*, but, somewhat inconsistently, we would then include it in the family Eurotiaceae of the Eurotiales. Strict adherence to the International Code of Nomenclature apparently directs us, on the contrary, to place it in an ascomycetous genus. Raper and Thom (1949, p. 574) have allied it with the *P. luteum* series "upon the bases of its biverticillate penicilli with conspicuously lanceolate sterigmata bearing strongly elliptical conidia and its perithecia with soft plectenchymatous walls." Benjamin (1955), in his proposed reassignment of all perfect penicillia to ascomycetous genera, might, therefore, logically have included *P. duponti* in his genus *Talaromyces*, along with *P. luteum*. For reasons not clear to us he actually made no reference at all to *P. duponti*.

Evidently we must take our own stand here. Acceptance of Raper's (1957) point of view, attractive as it is in some respects, seems to us to

Plate 1.
(**Above**) Cleistothecia of *Talaromyces* (*Penicillium*) *duponti* in pure culture on chopped guayule shrub, incubated 14 days. ×16. (**Below**) Cleistothecia of *Talaromyces* (*Penicillium*) *duponti*, dissected out to show the globose shape and general range of size. ×16.

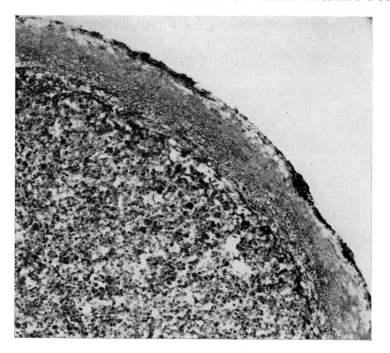

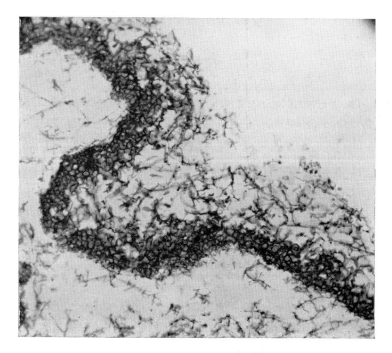

strike at the very foundation of the cumbersome but essential nomenclature of perfect and imperfect fungi. Until, therefore, some better over-all scheme is devised and put into effect by incorporation into the Code of Nomenclature, we feel obliged to assign to *Penicillium duponti* the name *Talaromyces duponti*. If both perfect and imperfect names—such as *Talaromyces (Penicillium) duponti*—were consistently used together in the future, much of the confusion about which Raper is so justly concerned could readily be avoided.

Here it should also be noted that positive assignment of *P. duponti* to *Talaromyces* must depend upon information still to be gathered. In defining his genera, Benjamin (1955) placed considerable emphasis upon the details of ascocarp initiation and ascus formation. These details remain to be worked out for *P. duponti*, so that, ironically, the nomenclature we have proposed here rests in part upon the judgment of Raper and Thom (1949) that *Penicillium duponti* is in the *P. luteum* series! The species does, however, lack the bright yellow or orange pigmentation so characteristic of many members of that series. Moreover, no other species in the series, as treated by Raper and Thom (1949), has ascospores with a distinct, pulley-like, equatorial groove or cleistothecia with such determinate growth and markedly thick walls. Above all, *P. duponti* stands out among the great assemblage of species of *Penicillium* as the only accepted species to have evolved the thermophilic habit.

In 1939 Mal'chevskaya reported the isolation, from self-heating peat in Russia, of a fungus that grew optimally at 50°C and only very poorly at 25–28°C. This was evidently a true thermophile with the basic characters of a *Penicillium*: mycelium composed of septate hyphae 2.5–3.5 μ wide; a septate conidiophore (shown in Fig. 1 of Mal'chevskaya, 1939) arising as a lateral branch at right angles to the vegetative hypha, about 50 × 3 μ, itself branched once in the distal part and bearing two monoverticillate penicilli on its very slightly swollen apices; phialides 10 μ long; conidia in chains and 3.0–3.5 × 2.5–2.8 μ. The growth on laboratory media is described as fleecy, first white then a sandy hue with a faint, light brick-red tint. In age, white overgrowths are formed. Comparison with our description shows that this mold from peat, so far as can be determined from the limited ac-

Plate 2.

(**Above**) Cross section of nearly mature cleistothecium of *Talaromyces (Penicillium) duponti*, showing smooth plectenchymatous peridium and ascospores within. ×236. (**Below**) Cross section of mature cleistothecium of *Thermoascus aurantiacus*, showing irregular pseudoparenchymatous peridium and scattered fertile hyphae within; the ascospores were lost during processing. ×236.

count, is closely similar to *Penicillium duponti*. Mal'chevskaya named it *Citromyces sphagnicola* n. sp., but *Citromyces* was not accepted as a valid genus either by Thom (1930) or by Raper and Thom (1949). The latter authors were not aware of Mal'chevskaya's (1939) report of the fungi from peat, so we do not have the benefit of their expert opinion regarding the identity of *Citromyces sphagnicola*. We have concluded that it is a probable synonym of *Penicillium duponti*.

Finally, we must emphasize that *P. duponti* is not to be confused with *Penicillium arenarium* of Shaposhnikov and Manteifel (1923) or any of the various other possibly thermophilic fungi allied to *Paecilomyces*. These forms are discussed in a subsequent section devoted to excluded or doubtful thermophiles (see §13).

Diagnosis

Hyphae branched, septate, 2–3 μ in diameter; conidiophores short, lateral, usually more or less perpendicular to the main hyphae, simple or branched, septate, 5–30 μ long by 2–3 μ in diameter, generally tapering slightly toward the base; penicilli irregular, varying from monoverticillate with 1 to 4 phialides, to partially or nearly regularly biverticillate; metulae few in the verticil, 5–7 × 2–3 μ; phialides acuminate, divergent, 8–10 × 2 μ; conidia pale yellow, smooth, elliptical to ovoid, 2–4.5 × 1.5–3 μ; cleistothecia pale grayish tan, subspherical, scattered or irregularly clustered, 0.4 to 1.3 mm in diameter; peridium distinct, smooth, papery, nonostiolate; asci numerous, scattered, subglobose, 9–10 μ in diameter, 8-spored, disintegrating before the spores mature; ascospores lenticular, pale yellow, 3.5–5.0 × 2.5–3.5 μ, with a well-defined equatorial furrow flanked by low, smooth or somewhat jagged ridges, convex surfaces smooth or occasionally with ridges or irregularities.

Represented by specimen M206516 in the University of California Herbarium, Berkeley (our culture #26).

Temperature Relations

Next to *Humicola lanuginosa*, *Penicillium duponti* is the most strongly thermophilic of all the fungi. The temperature characteristics originally given by Griffon and Maublanc (1911) are: minimum, 25°C; optimum, 45–50°C; and maximum, 60°C. Our own observations on the isolates from guayule are quite similar. We could establish no growth at temperatures below 30°C; we obtained maximum growth between 45° and 50°C or slightly higher, and we found that growth ceased at or about 57° to 58°C. The cardinal temperatures can, therefore, be recorded as follows: minimum, 25–30°C; optimum, 45–53°C; and maximum, 57–60°C.

5

THERMOASCUS AURANTIACUS

Thermoascus Miehe (1907a, pp. 70–73)

SYN.: *Dactylomyces* Sopp (1912, pp. 35–37)

Thermoascus aurantiacus Miehe (1907a, pp. 70–73)

SYN.: *Dactylomyces thermophilus* Sopp (1912, pp. 37–42)
      Penicillium thermophilus (Sopp) Biourge (1923, p. 106)
      Penicillium thermophilum (Sopp) Trotter (1931, p. 671)
      Thermoascus isatschenkoi Mal'chevskaya (1939, pp. 26–27)

Thermoascus has been reported only seldom, and it too appears to be one of the rarer of the thermophiles. For this reason and because of its unique combination of morphological and physiological characteristics, we have examined it in considerable detail. It was first found on self-heated hay by Miehe (1907a), who presented such a comprehensive account of his pure cultures that there can be no mistaking the perfect stage of this unusual ascomycetous genus. Although Miehe observed the extensive white mycelial mat formed in young cultures, and studied the component hyphae very thoroughly, he reported that he had been unable to find any conidial stage. A few years later Sopp (1912), in the course of his investigation of *Penicillium*, again encountered *Thermoascus*, this time growing on a piece of wood being used to hold a thermometer in an incubator. He described and figured strikingly coarse conidiophores, with irregular dactyloid branches, and conidia borne in chains; laying emphasis upon this imperfect stage, he named the fungus *Dactylomyces thermophilus* n. sp. *ad interim*. Evidently Sopp knew of *Thermoascus*, but he states he had seen only abstracts of Miehe's work, and he does not list in his bibliography Miehe's (1907a) comprehensive monograph of the thermophiles from hay. Sopp designated *Thermoascus* as a possible synonym of his *Dactylomyces*. However, it is clear that *Dactylomyces* Sopp is, on the contrary, to be considered as a synonym of *Thermoascus* Miehe (see Taxonomy, p. 45).

Occurrence

Miehe (1907a) states that he observed *Thermoascus* frequently on markedly heated hay, in Germany. Noack (1912), on the other hand, was unable to locate it on hay but did succeed in finding it in a compost of leaves in the Leipzig Botanical Garden where, he reports, it had also been found some time previously by P. Schneider. In the meantime Sopp (1912), in Norway, had discovered his *Dactylomyces*, which appeared fortuitously when an old piece of damp beech-wood was placed in an incubator. After these early reports, we have found no further published records of the occurrence of *Thermoascus* until 1936, when Isachenko and Mal'chevskaya reported *T. aurantiacus* on spontaneously heated peat in Russia. Subsequently, Mal'chevskaya (1939), in presenting an account of the cultural behavior and morphology of this fungus, referred to it as "*T. isatschenkoi* sp. nov." (see below).

A further record of *Thermoascus* should also be noted here. The culture list (1957) of the Centraalbureau voor Schimmelcultures at Baarn, Holland, includes two strains of *T. aurantiacus* Miehe, one designated "Noack," the other "C.B.S." Miss A. L. van Beverwijk, then Director of the Collection, informed us (letter of January 28, 1960) that the first strain was received from Noack in 1931. Unfortunately no further information on the origin of this strain appears to be available. However, since Miehe stated in 1930 (1930a, p. 96) that he had no viable cultures of *Thermoascus* at that time, and since Noack had himself isolated a strain in 1912 and reported extensive physiological studies with it in 1920, we may surmise that the Baarn strain is Noack's own and not Miehe's (1907a) original one. This assumption is further borne out by the ascospores of the Baarn strain, which are about 1.5 times as large as those reported by Miehe for his 1907 isolate (see Table 3).

The second strain, Miss van Beverwijk writes, "was isolated by Dr. G. E. Bunschoten in September 1934 from cacao husks used as covering material on seed beds in a hothouse." Presumably the hothouse was in Holland, but the actual geographical origin of the fungus—whether indigenous or introduced on the cacao—must remain in doubt. At any rate, its occurrence on chocolate pods is most interesting.

The general rarity of *Thermoascus* is emphasized by Crisan's (1959) report that he never came across it in his extensive studies. During the entire course of our own investigations, it was detected only under the special conditions developed in a deep, standing (unturned) ret of chopped guayule shrub. Our isolate was made in June, 1945, at Salinas, California, from a conspicuous, extensive growth that occurred eight feet below the surface of the retting material. In this experiment the defoliated guayule had been cut to half-inch pieces and loaded into a cylindrical wooden bin about four feet in diameter and twenty feet high. The chopped shrub had a moisture content of about 40 percent at the start of the ret. It was force-ventilated with moist air during the seven days of the ret, at the end of which time the moisture had dropped to about 26 percent. Daily records showed that the temperatures within the central parts of the shrub mass had risen to around 60°C in the early phases of the ret. The *p*H of the retted material was 7.3 when samples were taken at the end of the run.

The appearance of *Thermoascus* on the guayule was much as Miehe (1907a) had described it on hay. Rusty orange, speckled patches are noted at once when the moldy plant material is broken open. The color results from the formation of numerous, small, yellow to reddish, cleistothecial masses scattered over the bits of substratum. No conspicuous mycelium can be associated with the reproductive organs at this time.

Like Miehe (1907a), we encountered some difficulty in our first efforts to obtain cultures. All the initial isolates, made on OA agar and other media, were contaminated with *Aspergillus fumigatus*, a thermotolerant species often widespread in the retted shrub. When, however, more careful asco-spore isolations were made from retted, dried shrub to YG agar and C3 agar, and the cultures were held at 37° and 45°C, rapid growth of *Thermoascus* occurred and pure cultures were obtained.

Morphology and Cultural Characteristics

The following description is based upon material grown in pure cultures at 37°C on YG or OA agar. Our observations are in general agreement with most of the detailed features so fully reported by Miehe (1907a) and Sopp (1912). A few discrepancies will be noted below. The initial growth of vegetative mycelium at optimum temperatures is very rapid and extends outward from a central inoculum to reach the periphery of a 10-cm petri dish in two or three days. At first the hyphae are largely within the sub-stratum or closely spread over the surface. By the third or fourth day, however, a conspicuous change has become evident. A scattered growth

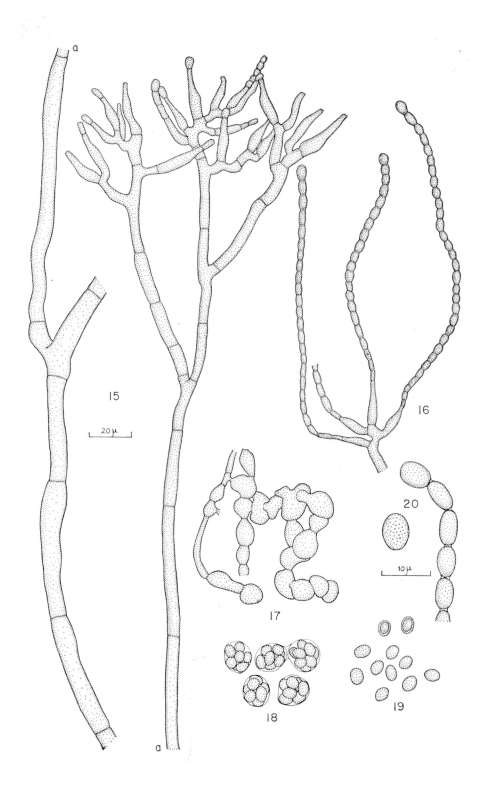

15

20µ

16

17

20

10µ

18

19

a

a

of coarse, branched hyphae has arisen from the basal mycelium and extends up from the surface of the culture as much as five or ten mm, often reaching the petri dish lid. The culture at this stage is nearly pure white or very pale gray-buff, and the loose network of partly trailing and partly erect aerial hyphae looks quite mucoraceous. Microscopic examination of such cultures reveals the coarse, dactyloid conidiophores that arise as terminal branches of these aerial hyphae.

The conidiophore stalks (Fig. 15), which may be as long as 1000 μ, are septate and irregularly branched. They taper from about 10 or 12 μ in diameter at the base to about 5 μ at their apices just below the phialides. Individual cells may be as short as 20 μ or as long as 75 or 100 μ. The phialides (Figs. 15 and 16), which suggested to Sopp the name *Dactylomyces*, are indeed very irregularly arranged and sometimes actually branched. Close scrutiny reveals, however, that the crosswalls between the phialides and the cells immediately below them are very delicate and can easily be overlooked. It seems likely that the phialides themselves are actually much less branched than one could conclude from Sopp's (1912, Taf. III) striking though somewhat sketchy illustrations. The elongate, flask-shaped phialides are 15–28 μ long and 3–7 μ in diameter at their widest point.

Long, loosely tangled chains of conidia (Figs. 16 and 20) are formed on the phialides in the manner characteristic of *Penicillium* and related genera. When newly formed they are subcylindric, 4.5–7.0 μ long and 2.0–2.5 μ broad. As they mature they swell somewhat, become elliptical, and ultimately measure 6–7 $\times$ 4–5 μ. They have an extremely thin, smooth wall, which suggests that they possess little capacity for carryover or resistance to adverse conditions. The conidia appear to be almost devoid of color, but they sometimes look pale ocher by reflected light. As shown in Fig. 20, high magnification reveals inconspicuous connectives or disjunctor regions between the mature conidia (compare Raper and Thom, 1949, p. 51).

This striking conidial apparatus is amazingly delicate and evanescent. Merely opening the lid of a petri dish culture at this stage soon results in

---

Figs. 15–20. *Thermoascus aurantiacus.*

Fig. 15. Long branched conidiophore bearing irregularly digitate phialides at its apex. Fig. 16. A cluster of phialides with chains of developing conidia. Fig. 17. Large pseudoparenchymatous cells forming the outer peridial layer of the cleistothecium. Fig. 18. Several asci with maturing ascospores. Fig. 19. Mature ascospores (two in optical section) released from the evanescent asci. Fig. 20. Enlarged view of an ascospore, showing the very fine wall sculpturing, and a chain of mature conidia with inconspicuous connectives.

complete collapse of the aerial system. Moreover, the conidial stage is probably very fugacious in nature because it disappears almost entirely in laboratory culture within a day or two of its peak development. This suggests one possible reason why Miehe (1907a) failed to see any conidiophores in his *Thermoascus*.

Production of the ascogenous phase of *Thermoascus* also takes place with astonishing rapidity. Sometimes as early as the second day, and certainly by the third, cleistothecial initials become evident as small granular masses of knotted hyphae in the white surface mycelium. Within the next two or three days a marked change occurs in the appearance of the culture. Directly following the collapse and virtual disappearance of the conidial apparatus, the speckled or granular surface mycelium begins to take on a yellow hue. Then, as the pigment builds up rapidly, the color shifts to orange-buff, bright brick-red (see frontispiece), and finally, in older stages, dull reddish brown. At the same time the underside (reverse) of the mycelium becomes similarly pigmented, and glistening drops of golden liquid are formed on the upper surface of the culture.

All of these pigmentary changes are associated with the development of ascocarps. Unfortunately the early stages of sexual reproduction have not yet been investigated, so we do not know what sort of ascogonial and antheridial apparatus is produced. By the time the full reddish color has been developed, the cleistothecia are already mature. They appear on natural substrata (Plate 3) or in agar culture as irregular, globose, or somewhat angular, separate, or partly confluent masses ranging from about 0.25 up to 1.0 mm in diameter. The outer peridial wall appears dull and rough. Sections (Plate 2) show that the peridium is composed of several layers of irregularly swollen, pigmented, pseudoparenchymatous cells (Fig. 17) with somewhat thickened cell walls. These cells vary considerably in dimensions but are often as much as 15 μ across.

When recently matured cleistothecia are broken open, the difference between their red peridium and the glistening white spore mass within provides a striking contrast. As in all members of the Eurotiaceae, the asci (Fig. 18) are scattered within the cleistothecial cavity. They are 14–16 × 12–14 μ and disappear not long after the ascospores have been fully delimited. Each ascus regularly contains 8 oval or elliptical, 1-celled ascospores (Fig. 19) that measure 6.7–7.7 × 5.1–6.1 μ. The ascospore walls are conspicuously thickened (to about 0.5 μ), colorless, and nearly smooth. Critical examination with oil immersion has revealed some very fine sculpturing (Fig. 20), which appears to consist of minute, evenly spaced pits but might otherwise be interpreted as very fine echinulations (compare Raper and

Thom, 1949, p. 20). The ascospores of *Thermoascus*, in contrast to the conidia, are highly resistant and capable, when air-dried, of remaining viable for many years. We have obtained vigorous normal cultures from cleistothecia stored at room temperature for more than 14 years.

Taxonomy

Besides our own isolate, we had an opportunity to examine living material of the two strains kindly provided by the Centraalbureau voor Schimmel-cultures. In view of its penicillate conidial apparatus and its closed asco-carps with irregularly scattered asci, there can be no question about includ-ing *Thermoascus* in the Eurotiales or for that matter in the Eurotiaceae (Aspergillaceae). Biourge (1923) and Trotter (1931) placed Sopp's *Dac-tylomyces* in synonymy under *Penicillium*, but this disposition does not seem sound to us and was not accepted by Thom (1930) or Raper and Thom (1949) after they had examined our isolate from guayule. The irregu-larity of the phialides in the conidiophores and the coarseness and pale coloring of the imperfect stage as a whole are more suggestive of *Paecilo-myces* (see discussion of this genus in §13) or possibly *Scopulariopsis* (com-pare Emmons and Dodge 1931, p. 316). We believe, however, that the distinctive features of both the perfect and imperfect stages of *Thermoascus*, coupled with its pronounced thermophilic character, justify its retention as a separate genus. More precise establishment of its relationships may ulti-mately be revealed by detailed study of the morphology and development of the gametangia.

   If the descriptions of Miehe (1907a), Sopp (1912), and ourselves are compared point by point they will be found to agree in large measure. However, a number of small differences also become apparent and one must consider whether these are sufficiently large and clear-cut to provide any bases for specific differentiation. Evaluation of the evidence is com-plicated by the lack of precision in Sopp's observations. His magnifications are never exactly indicated but are only suggested by the lens combinations used. From this and the generally sketchy nature of his drawings, one must conclude that he did not use a camera lucida. The main points of compari-son we have considered are these.

   1. *Ascocarp ostiole.* The production of a regular ostiolar opening in the ascocarp would be a feature of basic taxonomic importance and would probably necessitate removing *Thermoascus* from the Eurotiaceae alto-gether. Sopp (1912, p. 39) says that the ascospores at maturity escape

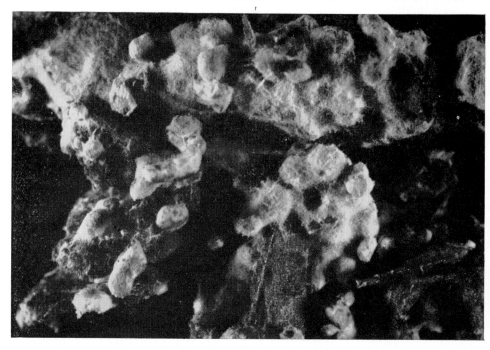

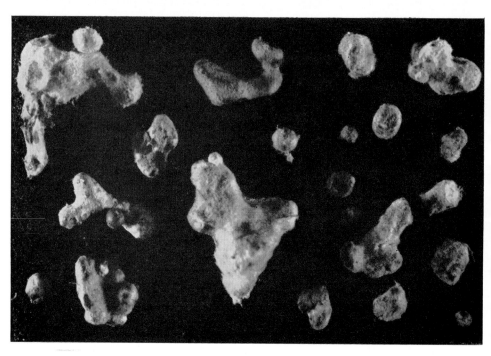

through a fine opening in the wall of the perithecium. Only in Fig. 25 (of his Taf. IV), however, is anything remotely like an ostiolar opening shown, and one certainly is not led to conclude that regularly ostiolate perithecia are produced. Thom (1930, p. 74) comments regarding ostioles in this group, simply that "Sopp's figures and descriptions show heavy walled perithecia, in some drawings including an ostiole, but lack details for further discussion." Miehe (1907a), who, as we have done, examined microtome sections of the ascocarps, makes no mention of an ostiole. In all of our own observations of three different isolates we have never detected a formed opening of any sort. We have, it is true, noted that the ascocarps of *Thermoascus* are somewhat friable and often become cracked open even from gentle handling. Possibly this provides a basis for Sopp's apparent belief that an ostiole might occur. At all events, we have concluded that *Thermoascus* is nonostiolate, and hence, following the terminology used by Alexopoulos (1952) and others, we have designated the ascocarp a cleistothecium in this genus.

2. *Presence of a conidial phase.* As we have pointed out previously, Miehe (1907a) found no asexual stage in his material. This may have been because the conidial phase is very evanescent and Miehe missed it. However, Miehe was an exceptionally close observer, so that an alternative explanation must also be considered. Our own stock culture of *Thermoascus* no longer produces the conspicuous conidial stage that it did when first isolated. Nor were we able to find any conidial structures in the two stocks of *Thermoascus* sent to us from the Baarn collection. Loss of the capacity to form abundant conidia is a well-known laboratory phenomenon in *Hypomyces* (Hansen and Snyder, 1943) and other fungi (Hansen, 1938) and doubtless occurs in nature too. It is entirely possible, therefore, that some naturally occurring strains of *Thermoascus* are incapable of producing conidia, and Miehe's isolates may have been of this sort. Further work will be required to resolve the problem, and until such time we prefer not to set up special taxonomic categories for strains with and without a conidial phase. It is interesting to note in this connection that reisolation of our own strain in 1952, from cleistothecial material that had been dried six years earlier from a pure-culture guayule ret, did give us cultures that again formed conidia in abundance.

Plate 3.

(**Above**) Cleistothecia of *Thermoascus aurantiacus* in pure culture on chopped guayule shrub incubated fourteen days. ×16. (**Below**) Cleistothecia of *Thermoascus aurantiacus*, dissected out to show their irregular shape and frequent confluence. ×16.

3. *Ascospore size.* The data presented in Table 3 indicate that the asco-spores are of two types. In Miehe's (1907a) isolate, and another strain mentioned by Noack (1912, p. 611), ascospores were reported to be 3.2×2.8 μ. All the other isolates have larger spores, falling essentially within the range 5–8 $\times$ 4–6 μ. We might use this difference, combined perhaps with the possible lack of an imperfect stage (see above), to establish a specific difference between *T. aurantiacus* Miehe and *T. thermophilus* Sopp.* How-ever, in the present state of our knowledge we believe it would be inad-visable to make such a distinction, and so we prefer to retain a single specific epithet until comparative studies of numerous strains have clearly established the occurrence of discontinuous differences.

4. *Conidium size and color.* The only other marked discrepancy in the various observations concerns the dimensions of conidia (see Table 3).

TABLE 3. Dimensions of the Spores of *Thermoascus* (in microns).

Strain	Mature Conidia	Ascospores
Miehe	Not observed	2.8×3.2[a]
Sopp	12–14 $\times$ 6–8	4×7–8
Noack	Not observed	$5 \times$ about 7[b]
		or 4.3×5[c]
C.B.S.	Not observed	4.5–5.0 $\times$ 6.0–6.5[b]
Ours	6–7 $\times$ 4–5	5.1–6.1 $\times$ 6.7–7.7[b]

[a] Noack (1912, p. 611) says he also found a strain with this same spore size but was not successful in culturing it.

[b] These measurements were made by us.

[c] Reported by Noack (1912, p. 611).

Sopp (1912, p. 38) reported that the mature conidia of his isolate were 12–14 $\times$ 6–8 μ, whereas measurements of our isolate fell in the range of 6–7 $\times$ 4.5 μ. This represents a nearly twofold difference and should not ordinarily be lightly considered. Nevertheless, because only two conidial strains have been examined closely, and because Sopp's observations are not always definitive, we believe here again that there is insufficient infor-mation for specific distinctions to be made.

Sopp also ascribed a greenish cast to the conidial phase of his material. No distinct green color was evident in our cultures although they some-

* The use of Sopp's specific epithet even in this case would probably not be allowed, according to Article 33 of the International Code of Nomenclature, since Sopp himself cast doubt upon the validity of his species by publishing it (1912, p. 37) as *Dac-tylomyces thermophilus* n. sp. *ad interim!*

times showed a pale gray-buff tinge. There may well be minor color differences between isolates.

Our general conclusion, therefore, is that the several fungi we have just compared can, at present, best be grouped in one species, *Thermoascus aurantiacus* Miehe, emended to include an imperfect phase and ascospores up to 7 or 8 μ in diameter.

In his later work on the self-heating of pure cultures, Miehe (1930a, pp. 96–97) describes what he tentatively named simply a "thermophilic *Penicillium*." He says that, in their efforts to reisolate *Thermoascus aurantiacus* (which, as noted above, they had lost in the years intervening since 1907), a Dr. Maeckel isolated a similar fungus with closely similar temperature characteristics—that is, showing good growth between about 35° and 60°C. However, this organism, besides producing a mealy crust of globose orange-yellow ascocarps, also formed a rudimentary (Miehe's word) penicillium-type conidial phase. A more precise description seems never to have been published, so we can only hazard a guess as to the true identity of the fungus. It seems not unlikely that this time Miehe had an isolate of *Thermoascus* that *did* reveal its evanescent, irregular, dactyloid (rudimentary?) conidial stage. Possibly unaware of Sopp's (1912) description of *Dactylomyces thermophilus*, Miehe was pondering upon the classification of his "thermophilic *Penicillium*" when it, like ours, ceased to produce conidiophores and thus made further study impossible.

Finally, we should state here our reasons for placing *Thermoascus isatschenkoi* in synonymy. This fungus was isolated from spontaneously heated peat and reported as a new species by Mal'chevskaya (1939, pp. 26–27). We are told that *T. isatschenkoi* resembles *T. aurantiacus* but differs from it in the color of the growth. The very scanty data and figures presented in this article do not, however, provide sufficient evidence for sound specific differentiation. Rather, the occurrence of minor color variants is again suggested.

Diagnosis

Hyphae colorless, septate, 1.5–12 μ broad; conidiophores erect, up to 1000 μ long, septate, irregularly branched, tapering from 10–12 μ in diameter at the base to 5 μ at the apices; phialides irregularly arranged, sometimes branched, flask-shaped, 15–28 μ long and 3–7 μ in diameter; conidia colorless, elliptical, 6–7 $\times$ 4–5 μ diameter, produced in long chains, the spores being separated by inconspicuous connectives; cleistothecia reddish brown, irregular, globose, or somewhat angular, separate or partly confluent, 0.25 to 1.0 mm in diameter; peridium dull, rough, composed of several layers of pseudoparenchymatous cells; asci numerous, scattered, oval, 14–16×12–14 μ, 8-spored, disappearing before the ascospores mature; ascospores oval or elliptical, colorless, 1-celled, 6.7–7.7×5.1–6.1 μ diameter, ascospore wall thick, finely sculptured with minute pits.

Represented by specimen M206516 in the University of California Herbarium, Berkeley (our culture #2).

Temperature Relations

Thermoascus aurantiacus, like *Mucor pusillus*, is not quite as strongly thermophilic as several of the other fungi we have included. According to Miehe (1907a) its ascospores did not germinate when held for one week at 25°C, and even at 30°C no growth appeared in four days. At 35°C, however, his fungus developed vigorously; at 40–45°C it grew best, displaying all of its distinguishing characteristics; at 50°C it still grew well but no longer formed spores; and at 55°C the growth was abnormal and very slow. Sopp (1912) designated the cardinal temperatures as: minimum, 25°C; optimum, 38–40°C; and maximum, 45°C. Mal'chevskaya's (1939) isolate from peat was similar: minimum, about 25°C; optimum, about 40°C; and maximum, presumably somewhat above 40°C but not clearly defined. Our own strain from guayule had a rather lower minimum, showing very weak growth at 20°C, a higher optimum at about 45°C, and a maximum near 55°C. It is likely that small differences occur from strain to strain. We may summarize the temperature relations of the species as follows: minimum, 20–25°C; optimum, 40–45°C; and maximum, 55°C.

6

MYRIOCOCCUM
ALBOMYCES

Myriococcum Fries (1823, p. 304)

Myriococcum albomyces n. sp.

Occurrence

We first observed this new and interesting thermophilic Ascomycete in 1950 on straw litter obtained from the nesting material of domestic chickens. The straw was moistened and then incubated at 50°C for several days, at which time the first evidence of the fungus appeared. Fortunately, good cultures were successfully started on YpSs agar from this original material, for repeated attempts to find the fungus again under natural conditions were not successful, although more recently a second isolate was made from straw obtained from the same locality in which the original material was found. Because of its thermophilic habit of growth, coupled with the apparent lack of a fine-spored, asexual stage, it appears likely that *Myriococcum albomyces* is not widespread in occurrence.

Morphology and Cultural Characteristics

On the natural substratum the superficial, nonostiolate, perithecium-like ascocarps developed after six or seven days, and when examined under the dissecting microscope they appeared as small, spherical, black structures scattered irregularly along the straw culms. Little mycelium was evident in nature except for a thin weft running along the surface of the straw and some strands at the base of each fruiting body (Fig. 21). But on YpSs agar

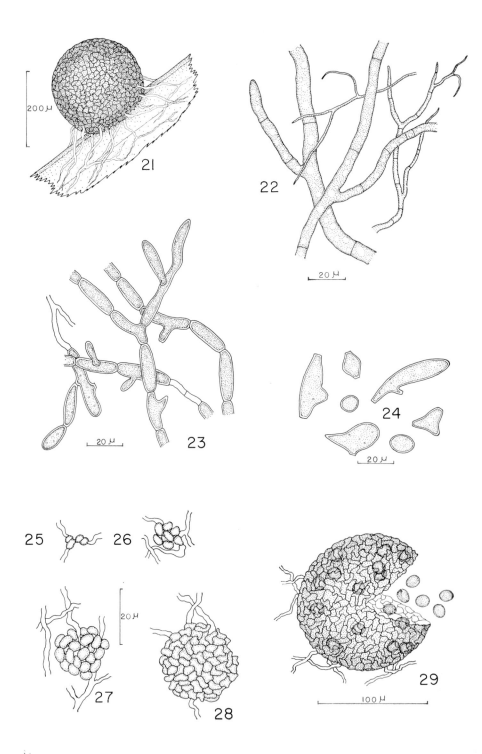

21

22

20μ

23

20μ

24

20μ

25 26

20μ

27 28

29

100μ

plates the hyphae form a dense, white, cottony subiculum surrounding the black ascocarps, which lie near the surface of the agar. In culture, the mycelium is seen to be composed of two distinct hyphal types. The aerial hyphae are septate strands, variable in thickness, ranging from thin threads, 2 μ in diameter, to coarse strands measuring as much as 12 μ in diameter (Fig. 22). The prostrate and submerged hyphae (Fig. 23) have a very different appearance, for here the threads are constricted at the septa to form chains of cylindrical, oval, globose, or irregularly shaped cells with thickened walls. These cells break apart easily when disturbed. Microtome sections through the mycelium in agar blocks show clearly that this type of hypha grows along the surface of the agar and also penetrates the substratum to a depth of about 100 μ (Fig. 39). Whether or not the cells of these peculiar hyphae function as true asexual spores has not been definitely determined. However, such cells serve to reproduce the organism, as do bits of broken hyphae, for they have been observed to germinate by germ tubes in much the same manner as ascospores or asexual spores.

If a bit of the normal mycelium is well spread out on a slide and then stained with lactophenol and cotton blue, the several stages of development of the ascocarp can easily be observed (Figs. 25–28). The youngest primordium appears first as a few oval cells clumped together along one or more hyphal strands. Subsequent stages show an increase in the number of cells, which results in rough, spherical structures with rather knobby-appearing surfaces. As these young structures mature, they become more nearly spherical, and the cells making up the outer wall lose their oval shape and become less regular in form. Mature ascocarps, which measure from 100 to 250 μ in diameter, are perfectly spherical when growing on agar plates but are usually flattened at the base when growing on straw. The fruiting bodies are colorless at first, then gradually turn light brown to dark brown or nearly black when maturity is reached. The outer wall of the mature ascocarp is glabrous with a slightly irregular surface, and is composed of cells of an indefinite shape. Although heavily pigmented, the wall is translucent in bright light and the dark ascospores can be seen lying loosely within the mature perithecium-like structure (Fig. 29). Since the fruiting body lacks an ostiole, the liberation of spores must occur either by mechanical destruction or weathering of the ascocarp. A majority of the

Figs. 21–29. *Myriococcum albomyces.*
Fig. 21. Habit view of an ascocarp on straw. Fig. 22. Aerial hyphae. Fig. 23. Prostrate and submerged hyphae. Fig. 24. Cells of submerged hyphae, showing variation in size and shape. Figs. 25–28. Stages in the development of an ascocarp. Fig. 29. Mature ascocarp with released ascospores.

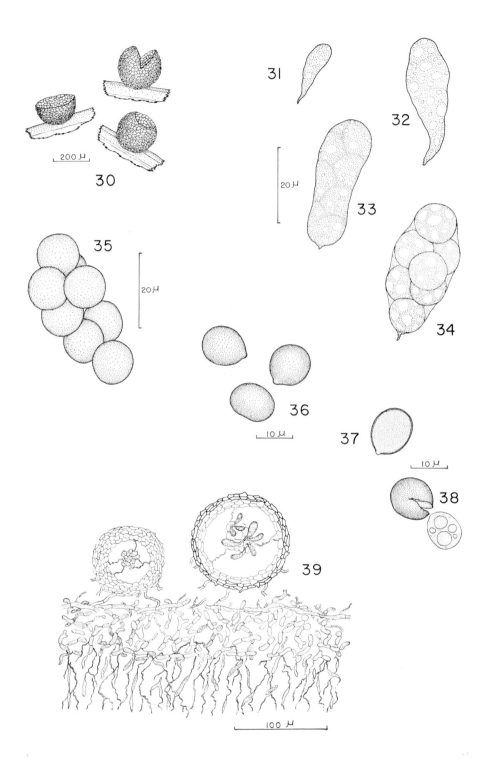

200 μ

30

31

32

33

20 μ

34

35

20 μ

36

10 μ

37

10 μ

38

39

100 μ

fruiting bodies in cultures over one year old were still intact, but many were marked by an irregular opening above, due to the inward collapsing of the upper portion of the ascocarp. A few had split in a circumscissile manner so that only the bottom half of the ascocarp was left in position on the agar. Mechanical pressure generally results in simple splitting of the fruiting body. All three of these methods of dehiscence were observed in fruiting bodies growing naturally on straw (Fig. 30).

The number of asci produced is variable, but it is generally rather low in most ascocarps. Generally from three to eight asci occur, and several fruiting structures were found to contain only one ascus. A great many ascocarps were completely sterile. Because of the fugacious nature of the asci, the estimates of their numbers were made by counting the mature ascospores in various fruiting bodies. The few instances where the asci themselves were observed agree with the above observations as regards the number of spore-bearing asci produced.

Immature asci are pyriform, becoming rather oval-shaped or oblong as the ascospores are differentiated (Figs. 31–33). The most mature stage of an ascus that was observed showed eight immature spores, irregularly grouped together within the thin ascus membrane (Fig. 34). The spores at this stage are spherical, with vacuolated, hyaline contents, and measure approximately 10 μ in diameter. Evidently the delicate ascus wall disappears at this stage in development. However, the ascospores remain grouped together for a time while maturation proceeds (Fig. 35). While clumped together the spores become yellowish in color, increase slightly in size, and assume a more elliptical shape. Mature ascospores are generally subglobose to elliptical and dark brown in color. They measure 12–15 μ in diameter (Fig. 36).

To determine the manner of arrangement of the asci within the ascocarp, microtome sections of the fruiting bodies were prepared. Seven-day old cultures incubated at 40°C on YpSs agar were selected for study, since

---

Figs. 30–39. *Myriococcum albomyces.*

Fig. 30. Habit sketch, illustrating irregular methods of dehiscence of the asco-carps. Figs. 31–34. Stages of ascus and ascospore development. Fig. 35. A group of ascospores after disappearance of the ascus membrane. Fig. 36. Mature ascospores. Fig. 37. Optical section through spore, showing thickness of wall. Fig. 38. Ruptured spore, showing the colorless contents and pigmented spore case. Fig. 39. Camera lucida drawing of microtomed material. Sections through the ascocarps show the nature of the wall and the presence of the central cells. The structure to the right illustrates the origin of tufts of asci from the central cells. The distribution of the prostrate and submerged hyphae can be seen in the lower portion of the section.

more asci were usually evident in cultures of this age than in younger or older material. Blocks of agar 4 mm square and 6 mm long were cut from culture plates. These blocks were fixed in formalin–acetic acid–alcohol (FAA) and subsequently washed, dehydrated, and embedded in paraffin according to standard procedures. Serial sections of the material, 10 μ thick, were mounted and stained with aniline blue in 95 percent ethyl alcohol. It was found that this stain was easier to use and gave just as good results for the purposes intended as more complicated staining procedures. An examination of these prepared sections shows that, as the fruiting body matures, the inner cells break down and disappear except for a group of large cells directly in the center of the ascocarp. These cells remain suspended in the cavity by means of connecting strands that are fastened to the inner cells of the ascocarp wall. It is from these "placental cells" that the asci arise, in what appear to be one or more tufts (Fig. 39).

Crossing Experiments

Following the morphological studies on this organism, an attempt was made to determine whether the fungus was homothallic or heterothallic.

Because a relatively greater number of spores, capable of germination, was found to occur in older cultures, the ascospores used in the following study were obtained from year-old cultures. Six single-spore cultures were established on YpSs agar, and after an incubation period of ten days at 40°C they were carefully examined for the presence of ascocarps. Of the six vigorous cultures examined, mature, fertile fruiting bodies were present in only one. It was thought that this culture might not represent a single-spore colony, and consequently this one plate was discarded. Ascocarp initials were observed in three of the other plates but there was no evidence of fertile fruiting bodies at this time. It should be mentioned here, however, that after thirty days one or two fertile ascocarps were found in one of these cultures. But the fact that five single-spore cultures showed no evidence of mature fruiting bodies after a period of ten days—whereas hundreds of fertile ascocarps are ordinarily produced in five or six days in mass-transfer cultures—was tentative evidence of the heterothallic nature of this organism. This evidence was substantiated by a series of simple crosses involving four of the single-spore cultures. These cultures were arbitrarily assigned numbers from 1 to 4. Crossing was accomplished by inoculating separate sterile, YpSs agar plates with mycelia from two of the four different single-spore cultures. Each culture was crossed with itself as well as with each of the other three colonies. Table 4 shows the relative number of ascocarps produced as a result of crossing these four cultures in all possible combinations.

TABLE 4. Relative Production of Fertile and Sterile Ascocarps in Crosses between Single-spore Isolates of *Myriococcum albomyces* n. sp.[a]

	1	3	2	4
1	—	—	++++	++++
3	—	(++)	++++	++++
2	++++	++++	(++++)	(++++)
4	++++	++++	(++++)	(++++) ++

[a] Sterile ascocarps are indicated by parentheses.

The results of the above crosses clearly show that this organism is essentially heterothallic. Apparently cultures #1 and #3 are of the same mating type, which accounts for their inability to produce fertile ascocarps when mated. Similarly, cultures #2 and #4 are of another mating type, for crosses of these two cultures result in sterile fruiting bodies. When either of these latter cultures is crossed with either #1 or #3, a definite line of fertile ascocarps is produced along the line of union of the two colonies. Visible evidence of these obvious ascocarps is seen in Plate 4.

The fact that one or two fertile ascocarps have been found in single-spore and self-crossed colonies of culture #4 is evidence that this organism, although essentially heterothallic, has the potential of existing as a weakly homothallic fungus. Apparently *Myriococcum albomyces* is similar in certain respects, particularly as regards the nature of its heterothallism, to the much studied *Glomerella cingulata*, for in the latter fungus both homothallic and heterothallic cultures, showing varying degrees of fertility and sterility, have been observed (Wheeler and McGahen, 1952).

Taxonomy

The original description of the genus *Myriococcum* Fries, which is based upon the type species *M. praecox*, can be found in the *Systema Mycologicum* (1823, Vol. II, p. 304). However, Corda (1842, pp. 55–56) has given a more complete and accurate description of *M. praecox* and has in addition figured some of the gross characters of the fungus. The new species of

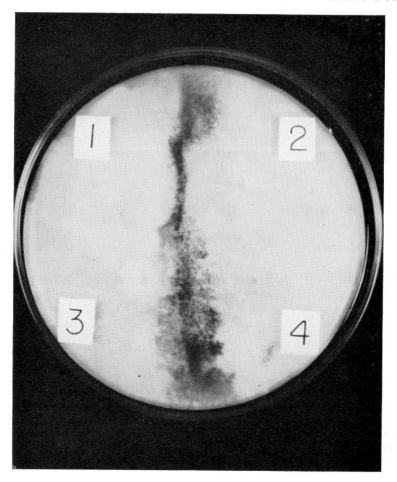

Plate 4.
   Agar plate inoculated with four single-spore cultures of *Myriococcum albomyces*.
   The dark line of fertile perithecia-like stromata can be seen to occur only be-
   tween cultures #1 and #2 and between #3 and #4.

Myriococcum described in this paper agrees closely in many respects with
the organism described and figured by Corda. Aside from the difference in
the size of the ascocarps—Corda records 50–70 μ in diameter for *M. praecox*, but the mature fruiting bodies of our fungus are 100–250 μ in diameter
—the gross characters of both organisms appear to be similar. The dark,
shiny, astomous fruiting bodies, associated with a white, mucedinous subiculum, are common to both of the species. Corda, however, did not observe the asci of *M. praecox* and obviously erred in his description of the

spores, which he lists as being transparent and polymorphic in shape and completely filling the fruiting structure. Apparently the "spores" described by Corda were the inner cells of immature ascocarps.

Following Corda's work on this organism, no further contributions were made to the genus for nearly half a century. In 1882 Saccardo and Ellis (in Saccardo, 1882b, p. 760) assigned a second species, which they called *M. everhartii*, to the genus, and shortly thereafter Harkness (1884, p. 42) described the species *M. sparsum*. The fourth and last species was described by Ellis and Everhart (1891, pp. 220–221) and was named *M. consimile*. Ellis and Everhart (1892) list the above species with their descriptions and have figured several of the morphological characters of *M. everhartii*.

Although all these authors treat the genus *Myriococcum* as an Asco-mycete, it should be pointed out here that, although correct, they were presumptuous in this regard, for no asci had been found in the fruiting structures of any of the four described species. From the description of *M. everhartii* it is evident, also, that no true ascospores were observed in this species, a fact of which Saccardo and Ellis were well aware. The pic-tured structures of their species, which correspond to the "spores" described by Corda, are designated by Saccardo and Ellis not as spores but as cells.

M. everhartii is similar to the type species in external morphology but has larger ascocarps (150–250 μ in diameter), which are clothed with a cottony layer. The fruiting bodies of *M. sparsum*, as described by Harkness, apparently contained true spores, these being elliptical and colorless. Evi-dently this is the first species in which spores were observed. The occur-rence of yellow-brown ascocarps, measuring 170–180 μ in diameter, and surrounded by a white subiculum, is in accord with the two previously described species. It is assumed that the ascocarps of *M. sparsum* are non-ostiolate, for Harkness makes no mention of the presence of an ostiole in his description of the species. The one remaining species, *M. consimile* Ellis and Everhart (1891), which was described as possessing an apical opening, appears to be an anomalous species and very probably should be removed to one of the ostiolate genera. Olivaceous, oblong spores have been observed in this species.

Because neither asci nor true ascospores were observed in the type species of *Myriococcum*, and because no asci have been recorded for subsequently described species, the genus has been considered to have no taxonomic standing as an *Ascomycete*. Engler and Prantl (1897, p. 308) treat *Myrio-coccum* as a genus of doubtful position, and Clements and Shear (1931, p. 248) list it under the category of doubtful genera. Ainsworth (1961) also questions the validity of the genus. Since we have revealed the presence of asci and ascospores in the thermophilic species of *Myriococcum* discussed above, it is now clear that the genus must be recognized as a valid member of the Ascomycetes. The failure of previous investigators to observe the presence of asci in any of the species of *Myriococcum* is readily understandable. It seems likely that early workers made their descriptions from colonies bearing ascocarps in either immature or advanced stages of development and overlooked the intermediate stages during which the asci were present. The possibility also exists that these workers were dealing with colonies in which only sterile ascocarps occurred, as is true of single-spore cultures or cultures produced from spores of the same mating type.

There now arises the difficult problem of placing *Myriococcum* in the proper order of Ascomycetes. Since the presence of a true ostiole has never been observed in the ascocarps of *M. albomyces*, nor have previous investigators indicated an ostiole in the fruiting structures of their species of *Myriococcum* (with the possible exception of *M. consimile* Ellis and Everhart), it must be concluded that the ascocarp of this genus is either a true cleistothecium or a perithecium-like stroma. It was thought earlier that the ascocarp of *M. albomyces* was indeed a true cleistothecium, which meant that only the orders Eurotiales and Erysiphales could be considered in placing this fungus. However, the presence of clusters of asci in the center of the structure did not make such an assignment feasible. Further study has convinced us that the ascocarp of *Myriococcum* is, instead, a perithecium-like stroma, which lacks a true ostiole but which opens irregularly or by weathering. The cluster or clusters of oval or obovoid, unitunicate asci, lacking a pore, then are borne in the center of the single locule that arises by digestion of the previously solid fundament. These characteristics appear most nearly similar to those of species of the order Pseudosphaeriales and, therefore, we propose to place *Myriococcum* tentatively in this order of the Pyrenomycetes, pending further clarification of the presently confused relationship of such pseudosphaeriaceous fungi.

Diagnosis

Myriococcum albomyces n. sp.
Hyphae colorless, septate, branched, decumbent to erect, forming a loose mucedinous subiculum in culture; aerial hyphae variable in thickness, 2–12 μ wide; prostrate hyphae constricted at the septa, forming branched, chainlike series of cells that break apart easily; ascocarps superficial, 100–250 μ diameter, scattered to gregarious, globose, dark brown, nonostiolate; wall glabrous, composed of polygonal cells; asci pyriform when young, irregularly oblong when

mature, 35–40 × 15–20 μ, produced in one or more tufts from a group of central cells; ascus membrane simple, very thin, early evanescent; ascospores one-celled, smooth, dark brown, subglobose or elliptical, with a single apiculus, 12–15 μ in diameter, irregularly distributed in the ascus.

HABITAT: On straw litter from a chicken nest from Reno, Washoe County, Nevada.

Myriococcum albomyces sp. nov., hyphis hyalinis septatis ramosis decumbentibus vel erectis, eis aeries diametro 2–12 μ eis prostratis septo quoque constrictis modo catenulato dispositis, ascocarpi in superficie auctis sparsis vel aggregatis globosis atrobrunneis haud ostiolatis diametro, 100–250 μ, pariete glabro ex cellulis polygoniis constantibus, ascis immaturis pyriformibus eis maturis ambitu irregulariter oblongis 35–40 × 15–20 μ in floccis ex circulo cellularum centralium auctis eorum membrana tenuissima mox evanescente, ascosporis unicellularibus laevibus atrobrunneis subglobosis diametro 12–15 μ in asci irregulariter dispositis.

Habitat in stramentis nidi gallinacei ex Reno, Washoe County, Nevada provenientibus.

Represented by specimen M206515 in the University of California Herbarium, Berkeley (our culture #5).

Temperature Relations

The temperature limits for growth of this organism range from about 26° to 57°C, with the optimum falling between 37° and 42°C. No growth was recorded at 25°C after four days, and only slight growth was observed at 27–30°C. Most rapid development took place at about 40°C, and there was a progressive decrease in the size of the colonies occurring at higher temperature levels. Small, dense colonies were evident at 55°C and slight growth was visible at 57°C. At 60°C no growth was found after an exposure period of four days.

7

CHAETOMIUM THERMOPHILE VS. ANIXIA SPADICEA

Chaetomium Kunze (1817, pp. 15–16)

> *Chaetomium thermophile* La Touche (1950, pp. 94–104)
> *C. thermophile* var. *thermophile* La Touche (*op. cit.*); var. *dissitum* n. var.; and var. *coprophile* n. var.

Occurrence

Chaetomium thermophile was originally isolated by La Touche (1950, pp. 94–104) from straw that was being incubated at high temperatures. Subsequent isolations of this fungus were obtained by La Touche from straw that was decomposing under natural conditions. In 1949–1950 we isolated two thermophilic Ascomycetes which, upon investigation, proved to be two distinct varieties of the recently described *Chaetomium thermophile* La Touche. We are proposing the varietal names *C. thermophile* var. *dissitum* and *C. thermophile* var. *coprophile* for our two isolates.

  C. thermophile var. *dissitum* was first obtained in 1949 from *Typha* straw used as nesting material by the common coot or mud hen (*Fulica americana*). A later isolate was made in 1950 from incubated leaf mold held at 50°C. After a two-day incubation period at 50°C, scattered, white perithecial initials were evident on the *Typha* straw. When observed two days later, the perithecia were nearly mature and contained asci and ascospores in various stages of development. Sterile needle-tweezers were then used to remove mature perithecia from the straw to agar plates. Although the organism subsequently grew on all standard agar media at 40°C, the most rapid growth occurred on YpSs agar.

C. thermophile var. *coprophile* was originally isolated in 1950 from a sample of horse dung collected near Berkeley, California. Later isolations were made from horse dung collected from several localities in the San Francisco Bay Region, and from one sample of horse dung obtained near Pyramid Lake, Nevada. *C. thermophile* var. *coprophile* has also been observed on straw incubated at 50°C. This organism was much more easily established on agar media than the var. *dissitum*. Even at a temperature of 50°C, growth was rapid and mature perithecia were produced in four to five days.

Morphology of *Chaetomium thermophile* var. *dissitum*

On YpSs agar at 40°C, the septate hyphae form a very thin turf, which at first is colorless. The hyphae, which measure 3–8 μ in diameter, soon become pigmented, and older hyphae are light brown in color. In mass they cause the colony to appear dark brown. Perithecial initials first become visible under the dissecting microscope in about two days, appearing as small, colorless knots on the hyphae. By the third day these initials have developed into distinct, erect, oval structures bearing straight, unbranched terminal hairs (Fig. 40). Generally the entire perithecium is somewhat hirsute, but the basal hairs are neither as numerous nor as long as the apical hairs. As the perithecia mature, the straight, stiff apical hairs change in form and become, instead, tortuous and dichotomously branched (Fig. 41). These branched tips often become loosely interwoven and thus impart a woolly appearance to the upper portion of the perithecium. The mature fruiting bodies range from 60 to 175 μ in diameter and are usually globose in form, although subglobose or oval structures are quite common. The color phases through which the perithecia pass in their development include the initial colorless stage, followed by shades of gray or gray-green and finally brown or dark brown. The perithecia are ostiolate, but it is usually difficult to observe the opening because of the dense terminal hairs. A careful examination, however, particularly when the ascospores are just beginning to be extruded, may reveal the outline of the ostiole. The perithecia are usually well scattered, although occasionally gregarious perithecia tend to form concentric rings on the agar surface.

Different stages of ascus and ascospore development can readily be ob-

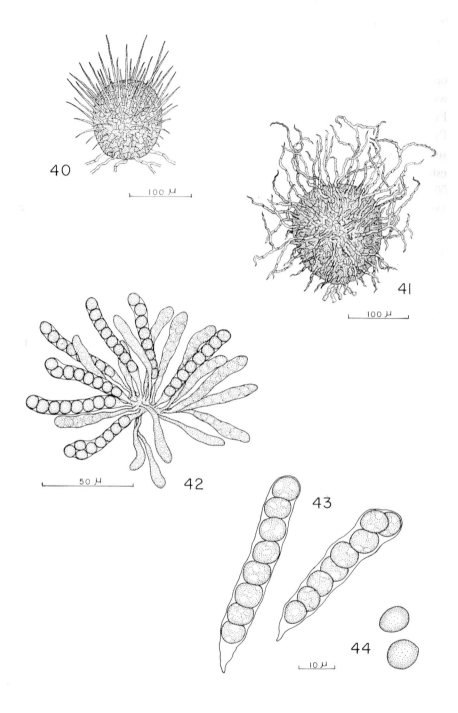

40

100 μ

41

100 μ

42

50 μ

43

44

10 μ

served by selecting nearly mature perithecia, or those which have not yet turned dark brown, and mounting them on a slide in lactophenol and cotton blue. When light pressure is put upon the cover glass, the perithecia rupture irregularly and the asci are squeezed out in a group. The short-stalked, cylindrical asci, which are produced in an obvious basal tuft (Fig. 42), measure 50–60 μ in length and bear eight ascospores in a single row. Occasionally an ascus may be found containing some irregularly arranged ascospores (Fig. 43). Mature ascospores are globose or subglobose and olive-brown in color; they measure 6.5–9.5 μ in diameter and are smooth-walled with a single apiculus (Fig. 44). When the perithecia are fully mature the ascospores are extruded in short cylindrical cirri.

Morphology of *Chaetomium thermophile* var. *coprophile*

The early developmental phases of this organism, when grown on YpSs agar at 40°C, are similar to those described for the above variety. However, growth of var. *coprophile* is more rapid and the resulting turf is deeper. The hyphae measure 3–8 μ in diameter and individual hyphae, when mature, may be light brown or may remain colorless, resulting in a grayish-brown colony. Mature perithecia are densely clothed with dark, dichotomously branched hairs and individually have the appearance of dark, woolly balls (Fig. 45). They measure 75–150 μ in diameter. Unlike the previously described var. *dissitum*, the perithecia of var. *coprophile* are usually not distinct but are instead imbedded in a dense, brown mat of mycelium. Individual perithecia can then be observed only by teasing away this layer of hyphae. On agar plates the cultures produce typical concentric rings of growth, the rings of dark brown perithecia being separated by narrow zones of whitish or brownish hyphae. This consistent zonal pattern is in contrast to the uniform colonies, producing scattered perithecia, that are characteristic of var. *dissitum*. Occasionally mature perithecia were observed, on agar media, bearing straight, stiff, unbranched terminal hairs (Fig. 46), but when the ascospores from these perithecia were used for single-spore cultures on separate agar plates they developed into colonies that produced only the normal type of perithecium. The asci are produced

---

Figs. 40–44. *Chaetomium thermophile* var. *dissitum.*
Fig. 40. Immature perithecium, showing unbranched terminal hairs. Fig. 41. Mature perithecium. Fig. 42. Tuftlike arrangement of asci. Fig. 43. Mature asci; the ascus to the right shows the less common, irregular arrangement of spores. Fig. 44. Mature ascospores.

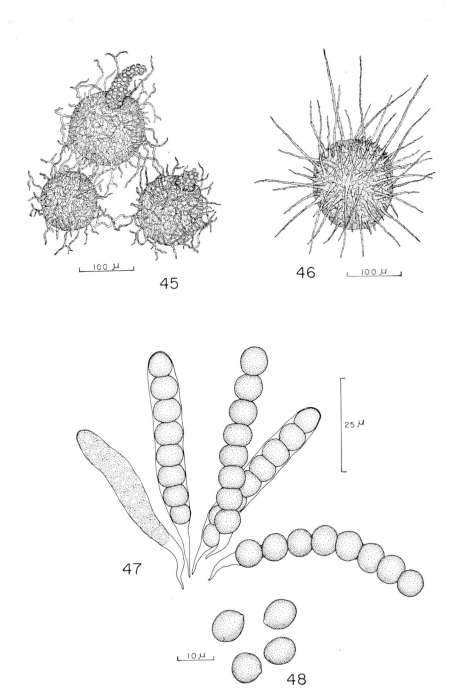

100 μ

45

46   100 μ

25 μ

47

48

10 μ

in a basal tuft; they are short-stalked and cylindrical and bear eight spores in a single row (Fig. 47). Irregularly arranged ascospores were never observed in this organism. Mature ascospores are usually globose or oval and dark brown or olive-brown in color. They measure approximately 8 μ in diameter (Fig. 48). When mature the ascospores are extruded in rather long cirri, which may measure up to 3 mm in length (Fig. 45).

Taxonomy of *C. thermophile* and Its Varieties

Shortly after we had isolated and subsequently studied the two thermophilic Ascomycetes described above, an account of a new thermophilic *Chaetomium* was published by La Touche (1950, pp. 94–104), who designated his new species as *Chaetomium thermophile*. After carefully comparing the features of La Touche's fungus with the characteristics of our two isolates, it was evident that the three organisms are similar. They all agree very closely in the size, shape, and color of the perithecia and ascospores. And the shape of the asci, as well as their arrangement within the perithecia, is similar for all three fungi. However, our first isolate, designated above as var. *dissitum,* differs markedly from *C. thermophile* La Touche in the growth pattern of the perithecia. Whereas La Touche has reported that his *Chaetomium* produces gregarious perithecia in feltlike patches on moist straw, our var. *dissitum* consistently develops scattered perithecia both on moist, incubated straw and on agar media. Such contrast in the manner of growth, we believe, is of sufficient importance to suggest our isolate as a variety of the existing thermophilic species *C. thermophile*. For our new fungus the name *Chaetomium thermophile* var. *dissitum* is therefore proposed. The second of our isolates, referred to above as var. *coprophile*, agrees with *C. thermophile* La Touche in regard to cultural aspects. The chief difference concerns the external appearance of the perithecia. In this new variety, for which the name *Chaetomium thermophile* var. *coprophile* is proposed, the perithecia are nearly covered with dichotomously branched hairs. This is in contrast to restriction of such hairs to the terminal portion of the perithecium in *C. thermophile*.

To justify the erection of his new species, La Touche emphasizes, aside

---

Figs. 45–48. *Chaetomium thermophile* var. *coprophile.*
  Fig. 45. Typical appearance of individual perithecia; extrusion of spores as cylindrical cirri is seen in the two larger structures. Fig. 46. An atypical perithecium, in which the hairs remain stiff and unbranched. Fig. 47. Stages in ascus development. Fig. 48. Mature ascospores.

from the thermophilic habit of growth, the presence of dichotomously branched perithecial hairs correlated with the production of cylindrical asci. Only three of the twenty-eight species of *Chaetomium* listed in the monograph of this genus by Chivers (1915) possess cylindrical asci, and all these species have unbranched terminal hairs. We have compared our isolates, as well as the description of *C. thermophile*, with three more recently described species of *Chaetomium* (Greathouse and Ames, 1945, pp. 138–155). One of these three species—*C. dolichotrichum* Ames—bears an outward resemblance to *C. thermophile*, but the spore sizes do not agree. Neither is there any mention of possible thermophilism for this fungus. There is no question that *C. thermophile* La Touche is a valid, thermophilic species. Our two varieties apparently represent the second recorded isolation of this thermophilic *Chaetomium* (however, see Addenda).

Diagnoses

Chaetomium thermophile var. *thermophile* La Touche (1950, pp. 94–104).

Hyphae septate, branched, at first hyaline, then olivaceous or brownish olive, 2–8 μ wide. Perithecia superficial, more or less gregarious, globose or subglobose, 75–172 μ in diameter, dark olivaceous or brownish olive; terminal hairs much branched dichotomously when mature. Asci linear cylindrical, short-stalked, 50–57 × 7–8 μ. Ascospores unistichous or rarely irregularly distributed, dark olivaceous or brownish olive, globose or irregularly subglobose with a single apiculus; 7–8 μ in diameter.

C. thermophile var. *dissitum* n. var.

Differs from *C. thermophile* mainly in the diffuse manner in which the perithecia are produced.
HABITAT: On incubated *Typha* straw and leaf mold.

C. thermophile var. *dissitum* var. nov.

Ab Chaetomium thermophile praecipue differt in modum diffusum in quem perithecia producit.

In *Typha* stramento folio putrescentisque habitat.

C. *thermophile* var. *dissitum* is represented by specimen M206513 in the University of California Herbarium, Berkeley (our culture #1A).

C. thermophile var. *coprophile* n. var.

Distinguished from *C. thermophile* by the dichotomously branched hairs, which more or less completely cover the entire perithecium.
HABITAT: On incubated horse dung.

C. thermophile var. *coprophile* var. nov.

Ab Chaetomium thermophile differit quod capilli ramosi perithecium totum paene tegerunt.
Habitat ad stercorem equinum.

   C. thermophile var. *coprophile* is represented by specimen M206514 (our culture #4).

Temperature Relations

La Touche has reported the minimum and maximum temperature limits for growth of *C. thermophile* to be approximately 27°C and 58°C, respectively. The optimum temperature lies at about 50°C. These figures agree very closely with those determined for the two varieties described above. However, slight differences were observed between the two varieties in the amount of growth produced at the higher temperatures. Whereas var. *coprophile* grows vigorously at 50–55°C, growth of var. *dissitum* occurs most rapidly at 45–50°C.

Anixia Hoffman (1861–1865; Heft III, 1863, pp. 70–71)

Anixia spadicea Fuckel (1870, p. 91)

At the time our two varieties of *Chaetomium* were isolated, and before La Touche had published his *C. thermophile*, only three thermophilic Ascomycetes had been described in the literature. Moreover, only one of these Ascomycetes—*Anixia spadicea* Fuckel—possessed characters similar to those of our *Chaetomium* isolates. Hence, a comparison of these isolates with *A. spadicea* was made to determine the extent to which they resembled *A. spadicea*.

Description of *A. spadicea* Fuckel

The original description of *A. spadicea* was made by Fuckel (1870), based on material collected from decaying straw. Essentially Fuckel's description is as follows: Perithecia hemispherical, brownish, nonstiolate, provided at the base with long, dark hyphae; asci cylindrical, 68 μ long (spore part), long-stalked, eight-spored; spores perfectly globose, yellowish, 8 μ in

diameter, with finely roughened walls. A later description of this organism
by Winter (1887, pp. 57–58), based on exsiccati, states that the perithecia
are 0.5 to 0.75 mm in diameter. The asci measure 120–150 μ in length
(spore-bearing part 70–80 μ) and possess very long stalks. However, drawings accompanying this description show asci that are obviously less than
100 μ in length and are relatively short-stalked. The spores are said to
measure 10–14 × 7–10 μ, which again does not agree with the measurements given in the original description.

The third description of A. *spadicea*, based on material taken from moist
hay, has been presented by Noack (1912). This investigator, who was primarily concerned with the physiological aspects of thermophilic fungi,
found that his organism was a true thermophile. Since this time, *Anixia
spadicea* has been regarded as one of the few thermophilic Ascomycetes.
The description of Noack's fungus, however, does not agree with either
Fuckel's description or that given by Winter. Noack mentions that the
perithecia are covered with grayish white hyphae, which give them a characteristic downy appearance. This is not in accord with previous descriptions
or sketches of the perithecia of *Anixia spadicea*, for only basal, creeping
hyphae have been reported on these structures. The spores of Noack's
fungus measure 8.0 × 5.8 μ and are smooth-walled and dark brown in
color. Here again there is general disagreement within the three descriptions regarding the size, color, and wall surface of the spores. Cylindrical
asci bearing eight spores in a single row occur in Noack's fungus. Noack has
also stated that the asci are long-stalked, but he gives no measurements
either for the length of the stalks or for the over-all length of the asci.

The brief descriptions of A. *spadicea* are compared above, not for the
purpose of criticizing the observations of these early workers, but rather
to point out significant discrepancies between the description by Noack
and those of the two previous investigators. This comparison is used as a
basis for the suggestion that the organism isolated by Noack was not a
species of *Anixia* but was probably a strain of *Chaetomium thermophile*
similar to the var. *coprophile* described above. Admittedly, one or two
points of disagreement are evident when the two fungi are compared, but
in most respects the two organisms are very similar. Except for the doubtful
existence of long stalks on the asci of Noack's organism, the internal morphology of the perithecium appears to be identical. Even the range of
temperature (28–58°C) within which the two organisms will grow is identical. The main point of disagreement is the apparent lack of an ostiole in the
perithecia of Noack's isolate and the presence of a poorly defined opening
in *Chaetomium thermophile* var. *coprophile*. It is quite possible, however,

that Noack could have overlooked the presence of an ostiole, for he was interested primarily in the physiological aspects of the organism and was only secondarily concerned with its morphology.

In addition to direct morphological comparison, we believe that further indirect criteria are of importance in suggesting the synonymy of the above organisms. Although *A. spadicea* had been studied in detail by workers previous to Noack, no mention was made of the need for high temperatures for growth of this fungus. Furthermore, so far as can be determined, no investigators since Noack have shown that *A. spadicea* is thermophilic. This lack of corroboration concerning Noack's observations on the above organism, coupled with the similarity of this fungus and our var. *coprophile*, has led us to conclude that Noack was probably in error in describing *A. spadicea* as a thermophilic fungus. This conclusion, as well as our previous assumption that Noack may have confused a thermophilic *Chaetomium* with his *A. spadicea*, could, of course, be substantiated, or refuted, by direct comparison of Fuckel's isolate with that of Noack and with our cultural material. Unfortunately, however, it appears that cultures of *A. spadicea* are unobtainable. Crisan's (1959) attempt to obtain cultural material of *A. spadicea* from several European herbaria met with no success. Until such time that *Anixia spadicea* Fuckel is recovered, and its thermophilic character clearly established, we submit that this organism should not be considered as a thermophilic fungus. (See also Addenda.)

8

HUMICOLA INSOLENS AND HUMICOLA GRISEA VAR. THERMOIDEA

Humicola Traaen (1914, pp. 31–33)

Humicola insolens n. sp.
Humicola grisea Traaen (1914, p. 34) var. **thermoidea** n. var.

Occurrence

Among the several imperfect fungi investigated during the present study were two forms which, although similar, are apparently two distinct species in the genus *Humicola*. The first of these organisms, designated as #3HF, was isolated originally from retting guayule by Allen et al. (1944) and was subsequently maintained in the extensive collection of retting fungi studied by Allen and Emerson (1949). A detailed investigation of this organism has led us to conclude that it is a new, thermophilic species of *Humicola*, for which we are proposing the name *Humicola insolens*. Our decision to place the organism in *Humicola* was based, in part, on the opinion of E. W. Mason, who has examined cultures of this particular isolate, and on the more recent paper dealing with *H. grisea* by White and Downing (1953). In 1946 a culture of #3HF was sent for examination to the Mycological Institute, Kew, Surrey. In a personal letter to Emerson, Mason indicated, in essence, that the culture most closely approximated *H. grisea* Traaen.

Recently we have received and examined in some detail a culture of a thermophilic *Humicola* originally isolated by Henssen (1957b) from stable manure collected in Germany. After examining the cultural and microscopic characteristics of this fungus, we have concluded that Henssen's isolate is identical with our *H. insolens*. So far as can be determined, Henssen's fungus is the second known isolate of this thermophilic organism.

Waksman, Cordon, and Hulpoi (1939) observed a fungus (in stable manure being incubated at high temperatures) which they believed to be a species of *Thermomyces* similar to the form described by Tsiklinskaya and Miehe. However, because of the insufficient detail presented by Waksman et al., it is impossible to identify their reported fungus accurately, and it is entirely possible that they were dealing with *H. insolens* or *H. grisea* var. *thermoidea*.

Humicola grisea var. *thermoidea* was first isolated in 1948 from elephant dung collected at the Fleishhacker Zoo in San Francisco, California, and incubated at 37°C. A second isolate of the same organism was made in 1952 from composting plant material obtained in Reno, Nevada, and a third isolate, obtained from mushroom compost material, was sent to us in 1952 from the Butler County Mushroom Farm in Pennsylvania. All three isolates were grown on YpSs agar at 40°C, and a critical examination showed these cultures to be strains of one species. Although this fungus, as typified by our three isolates, is similar to the fungus indicated above as #3HF, it is obviously not identical with #3HF. It also most nearly resembles the species *Humicola grisea*, but because of its thermophilic habit of growth it clearly is not identical with the mesophilic species *H. grisea*. We are proposing to place it as a variety of this species under the name *Humicola grisea* var. *thermoidea*.

Morphology and Cultural Characteristics
of *Humicola insolens*

As in most of the thermophiles studied, growth of this organism is very rapid under optimum temperature conditions. On YpSs agar at 40°C the thin, white colonies increase in diameter at the rate of 2 cm per day, and evidence of sporulation can be seen after forty-eight hours. The first indication of spore production consists of scattered swellings or groups of swellings along the hyphae (Fig. 49). As these enlargements increase in size they show signs of coloration, and about twenty-four hours later yellow-brown intercalary spores can be observed. Three methods of sporulation appear to exist in this organism. Probably most common is the production of intercalary spores, which may be produced singly or in pairs and occasionally in short chains (Fig. 50). Single aleuriospores are borne terminally on the hyphae or on short side branches (Fig. 51). A few lateral branches bear chains of spores. Immature spores are colorless or yellowish, turning light brown as maturity is attained. The aleuriospores are generally globose or subglose and measure 7.5–12.5 μ in diameter. However, flask-shaped aleuriospores 14–20 × 8–10 μ in size are common, and occasionally there occur larger, intercalary spindle-shaped spores, 14–20 × 8–15 μ. The color of the colony depends upon the age of the spores. Young cultures are white, but as the spores become fully mature the entire colony turns grayish brown because of a mixture of brown spores and persistent grayish hyphae. This grayish brown color of mature colonies is a consistent character and is in contrast to the jet-black colony produced by *H. grisea* var. *thermoidea*. Phialospores have not been observed in *H. insolens*. The above description and the line drawings for this fungus were made from subcultures of the original isolate #3HF growing on YpSs agar at 40°C.

Morphology and Cultural Characteristics of *Humicola grisea* var. *thermoidea*

When incubated at temperatures of 35–50°C on YpSs agar, *H. grisea* var. *thermoidea* grows very rapidly also; in thirty-six hours the colony will completely cover the surface of the agar in a small (6-cm diameter) petri dish. The colorless hyphae are rather fine, rarely exceeding 3.5 μ in width, and produce a thin, prostrate mycelium which is white in the initial stages of growth. Very quickly, however, the center of the colony becomes grayish as the aleuriospores mature, and in two days the entire colony appears dark gray. By the end of the third day the colony has lost the gray color and has become dull black. There is no evidence of discoloration of the agar by diffusing substances. Typical sporulation is initiated by lateral swellings at right angles to the hyphae (Fig. 52). These swellings elongate into short, lateral aleuriophores with bulbous tips. A crosswall then forms slightly below the tip and separates the apical part of the appendage from the basal section. This tip portion, which develops into the aleuriospore, then becomes rounded or oval in shape; the wall becomes thickened and pigmentation rapidly occurs, resulting in an immature, yellow-brown aleuriospore (Fig. 53). Mature aleuriospores are dark brown, smooth-walled, and generally globose, and range from 8 to 16 μ in diameter. But they may be oval, in which case they measure 12–16 × 8–12 μ. Pyriform spores of similar size are also commonly observed. Regardless of their shape, the

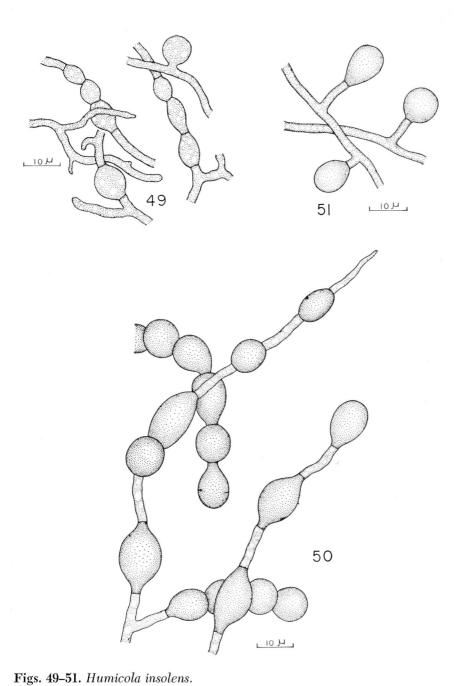

Figs. 49–51. *Humicola insolens.*

Fig. 49. Initial stages of intercalary spore differentiation. Fig. 50. Mature intercalary spores and chains of spores borne on lateral branches. Fig. 51. Mature aleuriospores, showing their development on short, lateral branches.

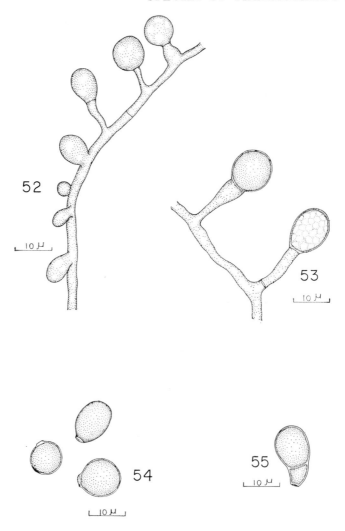

Figs. 52–55. *Humicola grisea* var. *thermoidea.*
Fig. 52. Initial stages of development of aleuriophores and aleuriospores.
Fig. 53. Advanced stages of aleuriospore development. Fig. 54. Mature
aleuriospore; note the typical flattened apiculus. Fig. 55. Two-celled aleuriospore.

spores are always marked with a distinct, flattened apiculus (Fig. 54). Phialospores have never appeared in any of our three isolates of this fungus. The
foregoing description and the line drawings of this organism were made from
subcultures of the original isolate (#48-1) from elephant dung.

Taxonomy

The genus *Humicola* as erected by Traaen (1914, pp. 31–33) included the two species *H. fuscoatra* Traaen (1914, pp. 33–34) and *H. grisea* Traaen (1914, p. 34). From the description of *H. grisea*, Mason (1941) has concluded that this species is synonymous with *Monotospora daleae* Mason, and comparisons of the sketches and descriptions of the two fungi support Mason's interpretation as to the similarity of the two forms. Mason has also indicated that the type species, *H. fuscoatra*, is very similar to *M. daleae*, except for the smaller, darker aleuriospores of *H. fuscoatra*. If Mason is correct regarding both of the above interpretations, then it would appear that the genus *Humicola* Traaen is invalid because of synonymy with *Monotospora* Corda. However, a clarification of the correct usage of the generic name *Monotospora* has not yet appeared in the literature. Corda first applied the name in 1837 to his genus, which was based on the single species *M. toruloides*. Apparently no type specimen was maintained, however, and subsequent workers were unable to duplicate Corda's find. Because of these facts, several investigators viewed the genus erected by Corda as an invalid one. Accordingly, Saccardo in 1880 proposed taking *Monotospora sphaerocephala* Berkeley and Broome as the type species of the genus. It was this change which brought about much of the confusion that exists today regarding the use of the name *Monotospora*. It would be sheer repetition to list here the various taxonomic shifts that have occurred involving this genus, for Mason (1933, 1941) deals with these problems in great detail and with notable competence. Mason (1933) has assumed that *Monotospora* Corda is a valid genus and has assigned the species *M. daleae* Mason as the type species until the original type *M. toruloides* Corda has been recovered. The culture selected was an isolate previously called *Basisporium gallarum* Dale, which culture, according to Mason, has been maintained since 1912 at the Centraalbureau voor Schimmelcultures.

At a later date, however, Mason (1941) indicated the possibility that *Monotospora* Saccardo might be accepted as the valid genus. This would, of course, imply recognition of *Monotospora* Corda as a *nomen confusum* and at the same time necessitate the recognition of *Humicola* Traaen as a valid genus. Mason (1941, p. 113) states, "If it is finally decided to use the name *Monotospora* in Saccardo's sense, *Humicola* will be the valid name for the genus differentiated in Fascicle 2 as *Monotospora* Corda." In correspondence with Emerson, in 1946, Mason wrote that he now thought it best to refer to *Monotospora daleae* Mason as *Humicola grisea* Traaen.

In accord with these views, White and Downing (1953), in their work with several isolates of *Humicola*, accepted *Humicola* as a valid genus including Traaen's original species *H. grisea* and *H. fuscoatra*. We also believe sufficient evidence has been presented in the literature for the acceptance of *Humicola* and, therefore, we are including our two thermophilic isolates in this genus.

Corresponding with us recently, C. L. Fergus has suggested that the organism we have described as *Humicola grisea* var. *thermoidea* might possibly be better included as a variety of *H. nigrescens* Omvik (1955). Fergus bases his suggestion mainly on the presence of phialospores in *H. grisea*, and the lack of phialospores in both *H. nigrescens* and *H. grisea* var. *thermoidea*. However, we have placed our isolate as a variety of *H. grisea* chiefly because of the uncommon occurrence of intercalary chlamydospores in both this species and in our var. *thermoidea*. Although Fergus' interpretation may have some justification, we prefer, for the present at least, to leave our organism as a variety of *H. grisea*. Our decision is based, in part, on the preliminary investigations of E. V. Crisan, who has informed us through correspondence that he has found gradations existing between isolates of *Monotospora*, *Humicola*, and *Torula*. The problems concerned with the *Monotospora-Humicola-Torula* complex can only be resolved when all forms, both thermophilic and mesophilic, can be studied and compared in detail.

It should also be noted here that in naming *H. grisea* var. *thermoidea* we are interpreting *Humicola* to be feminine. *Humicola*, literally a resident of the soil, is a word which may be considered either masculine or feminine, and indeed it has appeared in the literature both ways. Under these circumstances we believe it will be best to abide by the decision made by the author who first used the name. Since Traaen (1914) interpreted the name in the feminine sense, when he described the two original species *H. fuscoatra* and *H. grisea*, we are following him in the use of the feminine ending.

Diagnoses

Humicola insolens n. sp.

Hyphae colorless, decumbent, septate, 1.0–3.5 μ in diameter; spores smooth, colorless at first, turning light brown, variable in shape, generally globose, 7.5–12.5 μ in diameter, to oval, 11–17 $\times$ 7–10 μ, produced intercalarily or developed singly or in short chains upon short lateral aleuriophores. Differing from *H. fuscoatra*, the type, mainly in its thermophilic character, the common production of intercalary chains of spores, and larger spore size.

HABITAT: On retting guayule shrub.

Humicola insolens sp. nov., hyphis hyalinis decumbentibus septatis diametro 1.0–3.5 μ, sporis laevibus primo acoloratis mox pallide brunnescentibus inter se forma variantibus plerumque globosis diametro, 7.5–12.5 μ, vel ovalibus 11–17 × 7–10 μ, modo intercalari auctis vel brevicatenulatis in aleuriophoris brevibus lateralibus dispositis.

In frutice putrescente guayule dicto habitat.

Humicola insolens is represented by specimen M206524 in the University of California Herbarium, Berkeley (our culture #3HF).

Humicola grisea Traaen (1914, p. 34)

Mycelium thick, gray, entangled, quickly growing; hyphae 0.5–4.5 μ in diameter; chlamydospores colorless at first, later pale brown, globose to pear-shaped, 12–17 μ in diameter; conidiophores short, unbranched, thickened at the base; conidia oval 3–3.5 × 1.2–1.8 μ in diameter, in heads or chains; heads 5–9 μ in diameter.

Humicola grisea var. *thermoidea* n. var.

Differs physiologically from *H. grisea* in its ability to grow at high temperatures; morphologically dissimilar in lacking phialospores.

HABITAT: On elephant dung from the Fleishhacker Zoo, San Francisco, California.

Humicola grisea var. *thermoidea* var. nov.

Physiologice a *H. grisea* differit quad cresere possit; in forman differit, quod phialospores eget.

Habitat in stercore elephanti ex ferarum saepto Fleishhacker dicto in San Francisco, California proveniente.

Humicola grisea var. *thermoidea* is represented by specimen M206523 (our culture #48-1).

Temperature Relations

Maximum growth of *H. insolens* occurs at temperatures of 35–40°C on YpSs agar. The lowest temperature at which growth was observed was 23°C; the upper limit was 55°C. *H. grisea* var. *thermoidea* grows very weakly on YpSs agar at 25°C. Its extreme lower limit lies at approximately 24°C, and the maximum upper limit does not extend beyond 56°C. Maximum growth is produced within the range of 38–46°C.

9

HUMICOLA STELLATA AND HUMICOLA LANUGINOSA

Humicola stellata **Bunce** (1961, pp. 372–376)

Occurrence

This recently described thermophilic species of *Humicola* was isolated by Bunce in 1959 from moldy hay from England and Wales. Although the spores of this organism appeared in the dust from moldy hay, the fungus was actually isolated from a sample of hay, with a moisture content of 42 percent, which was incubated in a sealed tin at 40°C. The fungus was later transferred to hay infusion agar (20 g hay soaked in 1 liter of water overnight, strained, and 2 percent agar added). Bunce reports the fungus has since been found in numerous samples of moldy hay that have heated spontaneously during storage, from widely scattered localities in England and Wales.

Morphology and Cultural Characteristics

Bunce indicates that *H. stellata* grows and sporulates well, forming a dark colony, on hay infusion agar and other media containing peptone or beef extract. On media containing only salts and sugars, according to Bunce, it grows more slowly, forms a pale colony, sporulates sparsely, and produces colorless chlamydospores on the hyphae. Our culture of *H. stellata*, which was kindly provided by Bunce for study, grew well on YpSs agar at 37°C and produced a dull black colony. Microscopic examination showed the colorless, septate hyphae, about 2 μ in diameter, with short, lateral aleuriophores measuring about 3 μ in length. The aleuriospores, which are borne singly

Figs. 56–57.

Humicola stellata.

Fig. 56. Portion of the fertile hyphae, showing arrangement of aleuriospores on short, lateral aleuriophores. Fig. 57. Mature aleuriospores, showing the characteristic irregular shape; note the attachment piece on the two spores to the left.

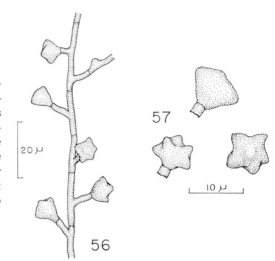

on the tips of the aleuriophores (Fig. 56), are subglobose and colorless when young, but become dark brown and stellate with maturity (Fig. 57). The mature spores readily detach from the aleuriophores and commonly the spores retain a short attachment piece (Fig. 57). Because of their irregular shape it is difficult to indicate a definite size for the mature spores. Bunce, however, has studied five different samples (each of twenty-five spores) and has concluded that the spores average 5.3 μ in diameter and 7.6 μ in length. The spore size for the culture of *H. stellata* we have examined agrees with these observations.

Taxonomy

If *Monotospora* Corda is to be rejected in favor of *Humicola* Traaen, as was discussed earlier, then those species now included in *Monotospora* Corda presumably should be placed in *Humicola*. Since *H. stellata* is very similar to *Monotospora lanuginosa* (Griffon and Maublanc) Mason, and since Bunce (1961, p. 375) has proposed transferring *M. lanuginosa* to the genus *Humicola* as *H. lanuginosa*, then her decision to include her new thermophilic species in the genus *Humicola* appears to be the only logical one. *H. stellata* Bunce is similar to *H. fuscoatra*, the type, except for the stellate spores and the thermophilic habit of growth of *H. stellata*. It is quite similar, also, except for the spore shape, to our two previously discussed thermophilic species of *Humicola*, namely, *H. insolens* and *H. grisea* var. *thermoidea*. It is interesting to note here that phialospores have never been observed in any of the thermophilic species of *Humicola*, whereas they have been reported for the mesophilic species, *H. fuscoatra* and *H. grisea*.

Diagnosis

Hyphae colorless, septate, 1.0–2.8 μ in diameter; aleuriophores short, 1.0–11 μ long, occasionally septate near the base, arising at right angles to the filaments; aleuriospores single on each aleuriophore, subglobose and colorless when young, becoming dark brown and stellate with age, 7.6 × 5.3 μ, separating from the aleuriophore and commonly retaining a short attachment piece.

Represented by specimen M209257 in the University of California Herbarium, Berkeley (our culture #61–22).

Temperature Relations

The figures below represent the temperature limits for growth of *H. stellata* as determined by Bunce and verified by our own limited observations of this fungus. Optimum temperature for growth is 40°C. Growth is very slow at the lower limit of 24°C, and the upper limit appears to be 50°C.

Humicola lanuginosa (Griffon and Maublanc) Bunce (1961)

SYN.: *Thermomyces lanuginosus* Tsiklinskaya (1899, pp. 500–505)
Sepedonium lanuginosum Griffon and Maublanc (1911)
Sepedonium thermaphilum cyclosporum and *S. thermaphilum
ovosporum* Velich (1914)
Acremoniella sp. Rege (1927)
Acremoniella thermophila Curzi (1929)
Monotospora lanuginosa (Griffon and Maublanc) Mason (1933)

This species is undoubtedly one of the most ubiquitous of the thermophilic fungi. Certainly it was the most commonly encountered true thermophile in this study. We have isolated it from a variety of natural substrata and it has been reported from widely scattered localities by several workers, as indicated below, during the last half-century.

Occurrence

The first known isolate of *H. lanuginosa* was made in 1899 by Tsiklinskaya,[*] who observed the fungus on a potato which had been inoculated with

---

[*] Also transliterated as Tsiklinski, Tsiklinsky, and (erroneously) Tsilinsky.

garden soil. Tsiklinskaya grew the organism on white bread kept at 52–53°C, and it was she who first described the fungus, to which she gave the name *Thermomyces lanuginosus*. A few years later Miehe (1907a) reported the species to be common on leaves obtained from warm compost piles, which were placed in covered dishes and held at about 50°C. Miehe, who included a more comprehensive description of the organism, assumed his isolate was identical to the species isolated by Tsiklinskaya. Griffon and Maublanc (1911) later isolated this fungus from moist oats incubated at 50°C. Although they recognized the similarity of their isolate to that of Miehe, they placed their organism in the genus *Sepedonium* as the species S. *lanuginosum*, since *Thermomyces lanuginosus*, according to them, was incompletely described earlier by Tsiklinskaya. Velich (1914) succeeded in isolating two thermophilic molds (origin not specified) to which he applied the names *Sepedonium thermaphilum cyclosporum* and S. *thermaphilum ovosporum*. The former organism, according to Velich, is identical with the thermophilic mold *Thermomyces lanuginosus*, which was isolated by Tsiklinskaya and which was also found by Miehe. At a later date, Rege (1927) isolated a species of *Acremoniella* from decomposing wheat straw (at 50°C) treated with assimilable compounds of nitrogen. Rege's description leaves little doubt that his isolate was the same organism studied by Tsiklinskaya, Miehe, and others. Shortly thereafter, Curzi (1929) obtained from moist grain a thermophilic organism which he named *Acremoniella thermophila*. This species has subsequently been regarded as the same organism studied by the previously named investigators. Other, more recent workers have also reported the presence of *Humicola lanuginosa*, particularly in composting material. These later authors uniformly use the original name *Thermomyces lanuginosus*, as proposed by Tsiklinskaya, for their isolates. Reese (1946) reported the organism in his study of the decomposition of cellulosic material, and La Touche (1950) noted the species on incubating straw at temperatures of 40–50°C. More recently Henssen (1957b) observed and accurately described the organism from stable manure. And Crisan (1959) succeeded in isolating it from composting plant material.

The first of our isolates of this species (strain #20) was obtained in 1945 from retting guayule shrub. Subcultures of this strain provided the material for the description and drawings in the present paper. Later isolates were made in 1950 from incubated sheep manure, and also from straw, collected near Reno, Nevada, and from composting leaf material collected near Berkeley, California. In 1953 several isolates of this species, obtained from mushroom compost material, were sent to us from the Butler County Mushroom Farms in Pennsylvania.

Morphology and Cultural Characteristics

This species was easily established and developed rapidly on most standard media, and little or no cultural variation was observed when colonies on different media were compared. The following description was based on pure culture material growing on YpSs agar at 45°C. Growth of this organism was rapid at this relatively high temperature and, after two days, colonies 50 mm or more in diameter were observed. The colonies appear white and felty at first, less than 1 mm high, but soon turn gray, or greenish gray, beginning at the center of the colony. Gradually the colony turns purplish brown, and at this time the agar substratum stains a deep pink or wine color, due to diffusible substances secreted by the colony. Mature colonies appear dull dark brown to black.

When young colonies were examined microscopically, masses of developing aleuriospores were evident on the fine, colorless hyphae. The rather short aleuriophores, which measure from 10 to 15 μ in length, arise at right angles to the hyphae. They generally are unbranched but occasionally they may branch once or twice near the base and thus appear as a cluster (Fig. 58). Septations commonly occur in the aleuriophores but they are difficult to observe. The aleuriospores are borne singly at the tips of the aleuriophores. Immature spores are colorless and smooth-walled, but as maturation proceeds they turn dark brown and the thick exospore (Figs. 59 and 60) becomes characteristically wrinkled. Mature spores are spherical, irregularly sculptured, and range from 6 to 10 μ in diameter. Both immature and mature spores separate easily from the aleuriophore. The aleuriophore usually ruptures slightly below the point of attachment of the spore, in which case free, immature or mature spores may be found with the upper portion of the aleuriophore still attached (Figs. 59 and 60).

Taxonomy

This species is still another thermophilic imperfect fungus whose taxonomy has been thoroughly confused because of the application of several different names. Tsiklinskaya (1899) originally isolated and described the species and assigned the name *Thermomyces lanuginosus* to the organism. Unfortunately, however, she failed to indicate the size of the aleuriospores in her somewhat meager description, and no drawings were provided. She did, however, include photographs of the mycelium and spores, but these

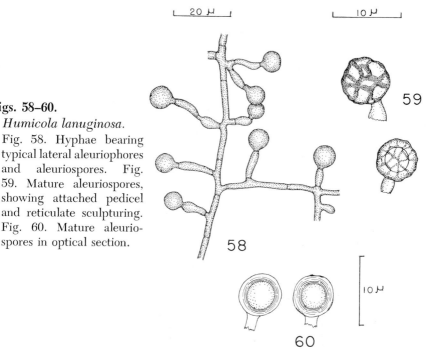

⌞ 20 μ ⌟   ⌞ 10 μ ⌟

Figs. 58–60.
Humicola lanuginosa.
Fig. 58. Hyphae bearing typical lateral aleuriophores and aleuriospores. Fig. 59. Mature aleuriospores, showing attached pedicel and reticulate sculpturing. Fig. 60. Mature aleuriospores in optical section.

58

59

60

10 μ

are rather inconclusive also, in that they do not give a true picture of either the size or the structure of the spores. If the magnifications accompanying the photographs are correct, then the largest spores shown would measure only 3.5 μ in diameter. This size does not agree—for it is much too small—with the spore size determined by subsequent workers. It appears, rather, that Tsiklinskaya failed, in indicating the magnification of the photographs, to allow for reduction in size of the photographs when the paper was published. This assumption on our part is borne out by the fact that Tsiklinskaya, in this same paper (p. 502) describes the hyphal filaments of a thermophilic *Actinomyces* as measuring 1.2 to 1.5 μ in diameter. The magnification of the photographs of these hyphae is reported to be ×800, and yet the largest hyphae shown in the photograph (Plate IV, Fig. 1) actually measure only about 0.72 mm in diameter; in reality, at the magnification indicated, they should measure about 1.2 mm. Allowing for this apparent error due to reduction, one can conclude that the aleuriospores of *Thermomyces lanuginosus* actually measure about 5 μ in diameter. This figure is near that indicated by other workers for the smaller spores of this organism. There is little doubt that Tsiklinskaya's thermophilic organism, *Thermomyces lanuginosus*, is the same organism isolated later by numerous workers and to which several different names have been applied.

Although Miehe (1907a) isolated and fully described this species and accepted the name *Thermomyces lanuginosus* Tsiklinskaya, Griffon and Maublanc (1911) refused to accept Tsiklinskaya's name on the basis that the organism was improperly described. They proposed instead the name *Sepedonium lanuginosum* for their organism. Velich (1914) ignored Tsiklinskaya's name *Thermomyces lanuginosus*, although he did credit Tsiklinskaya with first isolating the organism, and he applied the name *Sepedonium thermaphilum cyclosporum* to an isolate which he stated was identical to the isolates of Tsiklinskaya and Miehe. At the same time he gave the name *Sepedonium thermaphilum ovosporum* to a similar isolate. Rege (1927) used the name *Acremoniella* sp. for his isolate of this species, and shortly thereafter Curzi (1929, 1930) applied the name *Acremoniella thermophila* to his organism. A few years later Mason (1933) proposed the name *Monotospora lanuginosa* for this species, and although he lists *Sepedonium lanuginosum* Griffon and Maublanc, *Acremoniella* sp. Rege, and *Acremoniella thermophila* Curzi as synonyms, no mention is made of *Thermomyces lanuginosus* Tsiklinskaya. More recent investigators, however, as indicated previously, have persisted in using Tsiklinskaya's name, even though the more recent name *Monotospora lanuginosa* (Griffon and Maublanc) Mason was properly published and should have been applied to this organism.

It now appears, however, as was discussed previously in connection with *Humicola insolens* and *H. grisea* var. *thermoidea*, that there is a current trend toward accepting the genus *Humicola* over the genus *Monotospora* Corda, because of the questionable status of Corda's *Monotospora*. Consistent with our decision to accept *Humicola* as the genus for the two aforementioned organisms, we are following the proposal by Bunce (1961) to transfer *Monotospora lanuginosa* (Griffon and Maublanc) Mason to the genus *Humicola* under the name *Humicola lanuginosa* n. comb. Based on *Sepedonium lanuginosum* Griffon and Maublanc, the species would now be known as *Humicola lanuginosa* (Griffon and Maublanc) Bunce. Perhaps Bunce's proposal will clarify, once and for all, the nomenclature problem associated with this species since it was first isolated in 1899.

Diagnosis

Hyphae colorless, septate, 1.5–4 μ in diameter; aleuriophores short, 10–15 μ long, unbranched or rarely branched near the base, often septate, arising at right angles to the filaments; aleuriospores single on each aleuriophore, spherical, colorless and smooth-walled when young, becoming dark brown and sculptured with age, 6–10 μ in diameter, separating easily from the aleuriophore and commonly retaining a short attachment piece.

Represented by specimen M206522 in the University of California Herbarium, Berkeley (our culture #20).

Temperature Relations

The determined temperature range, within which our isolates of *H. lanuginosus* will grow, agrees closely with the results obtained by previous investigators. Optimum growth occurs between 45° and 50°C. No growth was observed at temperatures either below 30°C or above 60°C. In our opinion the latter figure represents the upper temperature limit for growth of true fungi, for none of the other thermophilic fungi studied produced visible growth beyond 58°C.

10

TORULA THERMOPHILA

Torula Persoon ex Fries (1832, pp. 499–500)

Torula thermophila n. sp.

Occurrence

The original isolation of this new thermophilic fungus was made in 1950 from straw, which had been used as nesting material for domestic chickens in Reno, Nevada. The description and illustrations were prepared from single-spore cultures derived from this isolate. Another strain was obtained in 1952 from horse dung collected near Petaluma, California. And in 1953 several cultures of *Torula thermophila* were identified among a number of unknown fungus isolates, from mushroom compost material, which were sent to us from the Butler County Mushroom Farm in Pennsylvania.

Morphology and Cultural Characteristics

Torula thermophila grows so rapidly at 40°C on YpSs agar that it ordinarily completes its development on small (6-cm diameter) petri dishes within four days. After forty-eight hours the white colonies—composed of thin, colorless, septate hyphae—usually cover the surface of the agar. When examined microscopically at this time, spores can be seen to be developing either as chains of intercalary swellings (Fig. 61) or as terminal swellings on the tips of short lateral branches. By the end of the third day mature, dark spores are numerous. At this stage the culture is grayish in color but it soon turns jet black as spore maturation proceeds. Eventually the entire mycelium is transformed into a mass of dark brown spores (Fig. 62), giving the colony the appearance of a thin layer of soot.

The typical mature spore of this organism is a spherical, dark brown, smooth-walled structure measuring 8–12.5 μ in diameter. Occasionally spores as large as 17 μ in diameter may be found. Atypical oval or spindle-shaped spores may be found interspersed in chains of globose spores. The majority of the spores are of a uniform size, however, and are produced in beadlike chains that are either branched or unbranched. When viewed under oil immersion in transmitted light, the double contour of the rather thick wall of the mature spore is easily discernible.

Types of Sporulation Reported for the Genus *Torula*

Mason (1941) outlines the three main types of spore chains that have been included in the genus *Torula*. (1) The phialomeristem spores or *conidia vera*, which are always produced in unbranched chains. Species exhibiting this type of spore formation do not conform to the type species and should be removed to another genus. (2) Dry blastospores, which bud off the swollen tips of a hypha and which usually result in branched chains. (3) Dry arthrospores, in which the hypha differentiates into spores from the tip backward, with branched chains resulting if differentiation includes a branch in the hypha.

Mason's third category of spore formation applies to the new thermophilic species of *Torula* (Fig. 63), although in some hyphae sporulation proceeds also in an intercalary manner. Such a condition is evident when mature spores are found flanked on either side by immature spores in various degrees of development. Chains of spores may also be tipped with a few immature spores that taper gradually into a thin appendage. Apparently this is the tip of an undifferentiated hypha.

Taxonomy

A review of the literature concerning the genus *Torula* indicates clearly that a modern, concise, monographic treatment is very badly needed to straighten out the confusion and synonymy that exist within this genus. There appears to be no general agreement at the present time, among the various workers, as to how many valid species there really are. Ainsworth (1961) places the number at twenty-five, but indicates that Saccardo has listed as many as 175. Obviously such a large number of good species, as the latter figure indicates, is not probable when one considers the simple structure of mem-

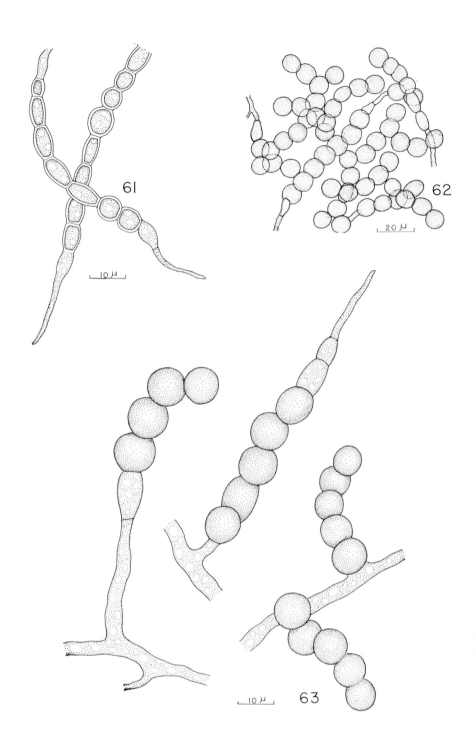

61

62

20 µ

10 µ

10 µ   63

bers of this genus. On the face of it, the figure given by Ainsworth appears to be a more realistic indication of the actual number of valid species of *Torula*.

Migula's (1934, pp. 211–221) treatment of the genus seems at present to be the most acceptable one, although the number of species listed here is probably rather high. Included under the genus are two subgenera— *Eutorula* Saccardo and *Trachytora* Saccardo. *Eutorula* includes those species having smooth-walled conidia. Migula lists fifty-one species in this subgenus. *Trachytora* is composed of the rough- or warty-walled forms, of which there are only two species.

Aside from the problem of synonymy in relation to the number of valid species in the genus, much confusion exists in the literature because of the persistent and erroneous use by some investigators of the name *Torula* for yeastlike organisms. The confusion regarding this usage dates back to 1838, at which time Turpin assigned the name to a type of yeast found in beer. Following Turpin were such outstanding investigators as Pasteur, Guilliermond, and Hansen, who continued the use of the name *Torula* for yeastlike forms. It is almost universally accepted now that *Torula* Persoon is the valid name of the genus and that this name should be applied only to those moniliform species possessing dark-colored spores. The genus does not encompass colorless spored forms such as make up the asporogenous yeasts.

Mason (1941) has recognized that Persoon (in Usteri's Ann. Bot., 15 Stuck, p. 25) properly erected the genus *Torula* in 1795, at which time two species were included within the genus. These species were *T. monilis* and *T. fructigena*. Dodge (1935) outlines a concise history of the genus in question, pointing out that Persoon (1801, p. 693) maintained the name *Torula* but reduced it to a subgenus of *Monilia*. At the same time he changed the specific name *monilis* to *herbarum*. Again in 1822 Persoon (1822, pp. 20–23) recognized the full status of the genus and added two more species, among which was *T. tenera*. In 1824 Link (see Mason, 1941) revised the genus, retaining only *T. herbarum* and *T. tenera*. As Mason (1941) has indicated, Fries (1832, pp. 499–500) accepted the genus and the species as *T. herbarum*. *T. herbarum* (Persoon) Link ex Fries, according to Mason, is undoubtedly the type of the genus, since this species has been in the genus from the time it was founded by Persoon.

Figs. 61–63. *Torula thermophila.*
 Fig. 61. Initial stages in spore development. Fig. 62. Habit sketch of a portion of a mature colony. Fig. 63. Chains of mature spores, showing the methods of development.

Ainsworth (1961, p. 408), in accord with the views held by practically all modern investigators, has summed up the evidence regarding the dual use of the name *Torula* in one brief statement: "Turpin (1838) did not make a new genus."

Because of the intergradation existing among the many described species of *Torula*, we find it difficult to relate, with certainty, the new thermophilic form to any particular one of these. The thermophilic habit of the new form probably precludes the possibility that it is identical with any of the described species. Therefore, we propose to designate it as a new species under the name *Torula thermophila* n. sp.

Diagnosis

Torula thermophila n. sp.

Hyphae prostrate, colorless, septate, 2–5 μ broad; spores dark brown, smooth-walled, translucent, generally globose, 8–12.5 μ in diameter, to oval, 10–12.5 × 7.5–10 μ, basipetally produced in chains on hyphal branches or developed intercalarily. Colonies white at first, turning jet black. Differing from *T. herbarum*, the type, mainly in its thermophilic character, the production of intercalary spore chains, and the smooth-walled conidia.

HABITAT: On straw litter from a chicken nest from Reno, Washoe County, Nevada.

Torula thermophila sp. nov., hyphis prostratis hyalinis septatis diametro 2–5 μ, sporis atrobrunneis diaphanis plerumque globosis diametro 8–12.5 μ, vel ovalibus 10–12.5 × 7.5–10 μ, modo intercalari vel basipetente auctis catenulatis in hyphis lateralibus dispositis.

Coloniae primo albae demum nigerrimae. Habitat in stramentis nidi gallinacei ex Reno, Nevada, Washoe Co., Nevada provenientibus.

Represented by specimen M206525 in the University of California Herbarium, Berkeley (our culture #3).

Temperature Relations

Evidently this fungus can grow within a wider range than most of the other thermophiles studied. Its lower limit lies at 23°C, and some growth was recorded up to 58°C. Optimum growth occurs at about 40°C.

11

MALBRANCHEA PULCHELLA VAR. SULFUREA

Malbranchea Saccardo (1882a, pp. 638–639)

Malbranchea pulchella Saccardo and Penzig 1882 (in Saccardo 1882a, p. 639) var. **sulfurea** (**Miehe**) **n. comb.**

SYN.: *Thermoidium sulfureum* Miehe (1907b, pp. 510–515).

Other synonyms of the species *M. pulchella* Saccardo and Penzig of significance in the following discussion are:

Malbranchea bolognesii-chiurcoi Vuillemin, Pollaci, and Nannizi (in Bolognesi and Chiurco, 1925, pp. 255–276, as *Malbranchea Bolognesi-Chiurco*)

Malbranchea kambayashi Kambayashi (1934, pp. 97–106)

Actinomyces bolognesii-chiurcoi (Vuillemin et al.) Dodge (1935)

Probably as frequent in occurrence and as much studied as any of the thermophilic fungi is the organism we are designating *Malbranchea pulchella* var. *sulfurea*. Our knowledge of *Malbranchea* dates back to 1882, when the first brief description by Saccardo appeared in Michelia. The genus was named in honor of A. Malbranche, a lichenologist and mycologist of that period, who had discovered the fungus growing on damp paper or cardboard in Rouen, France. Saccardo published an identical diagnosis, still lacking any figures, in the *Sylloge Fungorum* in 1886. It was not until 1907, however, that Miehe (1907b) isolated *Malbranchea* in pure culture, made the first comprehensive study of its morphology, presented the first illustrations, and demonstrated the thermophilic character of the strain he had isolated. Unable to ascribe his organism to any known genus, Miehe named it *Thermoidium sulfureum* gen. et sp. nov. Saccardo (1908) and Saccardo and Trotter (1913, p. 1240) promptly placed *T. sulfureum* in synonymy and were apparently unimpressed by the distinctive thermophilism of Miehe's fungus. Had Saccardo recognized this feature, considerable nomenclatural confusion might have been avoided in subsequent studies. Further discussion of the taxonomy will be reserved for a later section. Our own work on *Malbranchea* began in 1945, when a thermophilic strain of *M. pulchella* was isolated from retting guayule shrub.

Occurrence

Like certain of the other thermophilic (for example *Mucor pusillus*) or thermotolerant (*Aspergillus fumigatus*) molds, *Malbranchea pulchella* occurs naturally under two quite different circumstances. It is found growing either as a saprophyte on decomposing plant materials, such as leaf mold, cardboard, cordage, or retting guayule shrub, where microbial thermogenesis may or may not be conspicuous, or it appears as the parasitic causal agent of mycotic lesions in warm-blooded animals. Because present evidence suggests that the parasitic strains are not generally thermophilic, we will focus our attention here upon the saprophytic members of the group and consider the parasitic ones in our subsequent taxonomic account.

Unfortunately we cannot be certain as to the thermophilic nature of Malbranche's initial material. It is quite conceivable that there were special circumstances—associated compost, insulation from heat loss, or warming by insolation—any or all of which together could have played a role in raising the ambient temperature up to 30°C or higher. However, we have no record of such circumstances, nor were any cultural studies of that original strain ever made, so we do not know whether it was a true thermophile. The same must be said for the material Saccardo reported (1908) growing on decaying rope or string (*chorda putrescente*) in the Botanical Garden at Patavina, but we do have Saccardo's (1908) and Saccardo and Trotter's (1913) blunt assertions that their two collections differed morphologically in no essential way from Miehe's thermophilic isolates.

As noted earlier, the first demonstration of thermophilism in the genus came with Miehe's (1907b) detailed pure-culture studies of the isolates he was able to make repeatedly from self-heating masses of composting leaves or plant debris in Leipzig, Germany. Thereafter several other workers isolated this same fungus, grew it in culture, and clearly established its thermophilic character. Noack (1912) found he could obtain it readily, again at Leipzig, from moist grass cuttings that had been piled about 50 cm high and allowed to compost for six days. In the winter of 1944 Dr. W. W. Diehl (personal communication to us under date of November 12,

1946) discovered *M. pulchella,* for the first time in America, growing on composting elm leaves in Washington, D.C. Soon thereafter we ourselves came across it repeatedly in the guayule rets at Salinas, California. Conspicuous growths occurred in stationary, unturned rets on both whole and finely chopped shrub. In 1947 Rode et al. reported isolating it from composted manure in Austin, Texas. Crisan (1959) subsequently found it a number of times on composting plant material in the vicinity of Purdue, Indiana. Evidently thermophilic strains of *Malbranchea,* like *Penicillium duponti,* will also appear when suitable substrata are incubated at elevated temperatures. The fungus came up as a contaminant in a petri dish culture at 45°C at Berkeley in 1951, appearing on YpSs agar that had been inoculated with a culture of *Chaetomium.* Another time we observed it growing vigorously on goat dung being similarly incubated. Probably here too it should be considered simply as a chance contaminant. Other strains of *Malbranchea* have been found growing saprophytically, but they were clearly mesophilic in character and their relationship to the thermophiles will be considered below.

Where it has developed vigorously in decomposing plant materials, the thermophilic *Malbranchea pulchella* presents a very characteristic appearance, exactly as it was first described in detail by Miehe (1907b). Little flocculent masses of sulphur-yellow mycelium and spores are densely scattered over and through the substratum so that it has a typically flecked appearance wherever it is broken open. In older material the color tones down to a more drab mustard or brownish hue. We shall see that the initial bright yellow-orange pigmentation is also a characteristic feature of all the thermophilic isolates that have been cultured at optimum temperatures on media favoring vigorous growth. Miehe's choice of the specific name *sulfureum* was most apt and will serve well as a varietal designation.

Morphology and Cultural Characteristics

Several of our standard media provided favorable conditions for development of *Malbranchea* after pure cultures had been obtained by plating spores derived from natural substrata. The following account is based largely upon material grown at 37°C on YG or C3 agar plates. In the course of a week at this temperature the fine mycelium, starting from a central inoculum, grows out to a diameter of 5 or 6 cm and reveals a beautiful series of colors (see frontispiece) grading gradually from deep ocher-brown in the center out to bright sulphur-yellow at the periphery. Provided there has been adequate moisture, glistening drops of yellow liquid often form in the central areas and, when they have evaporated, leave the mycelium slightly mealy and irregular. However, the general effect is of a low, felty, even growth, less than 1 mm in depth and shifting quickly from white at the very outermost edges to the yellow color that characterizes the mature hyphae. The underside of the mycelium also shows strong pigmentation but here the color ranges from deep brown in the center to a wine-red at the edges. This reddish pigment usually diffuses out into the agar in considerable quantities.

In describing the hyphae, Miehe (1907b) noted that they were only sparingly septate and tended to develop quite conspicuous swellings (compare our Fig. 64) just proximal to the septations. He felt, however, that these swellings were of no diagnostic value because he had seen them also in *Thermoascus*. Similar structures certainly occur in many other fungi as well. Our measurements show that the larger, basal portions of fertile hyphae are 3–4 μ in diameter in the cylindrical regions, ranging up to 10 μ in the swellings. The irregularly spaced septa may be as close together as 10 μ or as far apart as 100 μ or more. Many hyphal segments are nearly 50 μ in length.

In their terminal, fertile portions (Fig. 64) the hyphae narrow down to 2.0–2.6 μ in diameter. They produce a system of characteristic, fine branches that are often quite regularly placed at right angles to each other or to the supporting hypha. Their ultimate tips are usually tightly curved into small loops or even short helices with two or three gyres, quite suggestive of the helical spore-heads in the Helicosporeae or certain of the Actinomycetes.

The young fertile tips, which are at first nonseptate and multinucleate, as Saccardo (1882a) had observed, now become regularly and progressively septate from apex toward base. In this manner there is formed by each terminal branchlet a row of small, blocklike cells (Fig. 64) measuring about 2–6 μ in length by 3 μ in width. Thereafter (Figs. 65 and 66), roughly every other one of these cells rounds up somewhat and develops an inner wall that approaches 0.6 μ in thickness but remains tightly united with the original, outer, hyphal wall. The alternate cells remain thin-walled, die, and finally collapse. A mature sporiferous coil, therefore, is composed of alternating thick-walled spores and thin-walled isthmuses. Our own observations show clearly that it is the final breaking of these thin-walled, sterile, connecting isthmuses that results in the separation and release of the spores of *M. pulchella* var. *sulfurea* in a powdery or dusty yellow mass. The charac-

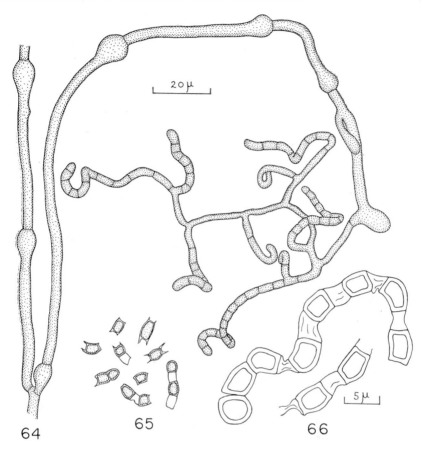

20 μ

5 μ

64   65   66

Figs. 64–66. *Malbranchea pulchella* var. *sulfurea.*
Fig. 64. Fertile hyphae with young conidiophores, showing coiled, septate
terminal portions. Fig. 65. Mature conidia which have been released by rupture
of the thin-walled isthmuses. Fig. 66. A mature conidial chain, much enlarged
to emphasize the distinction between the thick-walled conidia and thin-walled
sterile isthmuses.

teristic mature spores are generally 3–7 × 3–4.5 μ. They are subcylindrical
or often slightly curved or irregular and usually still show the angular shape
that results from their distinctive mode of formation. Viewed individually
by transmitted light under the compound microscope, they are pale yellow
or nearly colorless. No other spore stage has been found in any of the
numerous collections and studies of the thermophilic *Malbranchea*, either
in naturally occurring material or in laboratory culture.

Taxonomy

Three circumstances have conspired to complicate the taxonomy of this small genus. First, because they were not cultured we know nothing about the temperature relations of Saccardo's (1882a, 1908) early collections that include the type. Second, whereas detailed and thorough studies of the thermophiles and the mesophiles have been separately made, no single investigator has ever made a direct comparison of healthy, fertile, recently isolated cultures of the two kinds. And third, like most fungi, *Malbranchea* shows just enough morphological and cultural variability to defy neat pigeonholing.

Before stating our position on the taxonomy, we should note briefly the other collections and observations of *Malbranchea*. The first instance of this genus as a cause of mycotic infection was reported by Bolognesi and Chiurco in 1925. They isolated the fungus from a thoracic ulcer of a twelve-year-old boy, a resident of Ciggiano in Arezzo, Italy. Their description and figures, based upon careful observations by Vuillemin, Pollacci, and Nannizzi, leave no doubt that this is a species of *Malbranchea;* it was presented as *M. Bolognesi-Chiurco* sp. nov. The pathogenicity of this isolate was also well established by inoculations into white rats, development of characteristic symptoms, and subsequent reisolation of the fungus from the lesions. Ten years later Kambayashi (1934) isolated and studied another pathogenic strain, this time from skin lesions on the face and head of a Chinese boy living at Nanshon, near Shanghai. Once again experimental inoculations, into guinea pigs in this case, demonstrated pathogenicity, and the fungus was described as *M. Kambayashi* sp. nov. A third isolation was reported by Rivelloni (1938) from skin lesions on the upper lip of a man from Sardinia, but inoculations into guinea pigs failed to demonstrate pathogenicity. Despite this, Rivelloni assigned the isolate to *M. bolognesii-chiurcoi.*

Besides these strains that caused mycotic lesions, two other instances of saprophytic occurrence should be noted. According to the Centraalbureau voor Schimmelcultures (personal communication), the strain they listed for several years prior to 1939 as Buisman's *Malbranchea pulchella* was isolated by Buisman from wallpaper. There is no other information available, nor is there anything to suggest that this strain was thermophilic. Another saprophytic strain was isolated by Elisei (1940) from decomposing rice plants collected near Novaro, Italy. It grew and sporulated vigorously at 15°C and clearly was not thermophilic.

Now what can be said about the taxonomy of all these strains? Fortunately a very thorough comparative study of four of them was made by Baldacci, Ciferri, and Vaccari in 1939. They concluded that the Buisman, Bolognesi-Chiurco, Kambayashi, and Rivelloni strains were all so similar and agreed so closely with the original description of *M. pulchella* that all could be included in that species. They emphasized, however, that their collection did not include a representative of the thermophilic group and suggested that the latter might well represent a different entity. A summary of the pertinent data (Table 5) reveals little if anything in the way of morphological characters on which to base such a distinction. Nevertheless, the physiological difference between the thermophilic and mesophilic group is clear-cut and, at least at present, shows no significant intergradation. We think it will be useful, therefore, to establish a varietal category for the thermophiles, and Miehe's designation *sulfurea* can be retained for this purpose (see Diagnosis, below).

It seems quite possible that var. *sulfurea* will prove to be somewhat more robust than the type, generally more regularly pigmented in sulphur-yellow to brown tones, and consistently nonpathogenic. The type then would be more delicate, lighter in color, and might range from saprophytic to fairly actively parasitic and pathogenic. However, at the present time, the one outstanding character of the variety appears to be its marked thermophilism.

Several other taxonomic points can be appropriately dealt with here. First is the matter of possible relationship to the Actinomycetes. Apparently much impressed by the coiled fertile hyphae, Dodge (1935), in his monographic work on medical mycology, transferred *Malbranchea* to the genus *Actinomyces*. Suffice it to say that Dodge appears to have had no first-hand acquaintance with *Malbranchea,* and all subsequent students of the genus have denied the validity of Dodge's transfer. Baldacci, who was himself a specialist in the Actinomycetes, was particularly emphatic on this point (Baldacci et al., 1939). To our knowledge the Actinomycetes rarely approach the robust mycelial growth and spore dimensions of *Malbranchea.* Furthermore, the presence of discrete nuclei in the fertile hyphae of *Malbranchea,* as recognized in the original description by Saccardo (1882a) and further verified by Baldacci et al. (1939), supports the view that we are dealing with a true fungus rather than an Actinomycete. We believe, therefore, that *Malbranchea* must be removed from the position of synonymy currently assigned to it in the *Dictionary of the Fungi* (Ainsworth, 1961) and reinstated as a bona fide genus of true fungi.

Baldacci, Ciferri, and Vaccari (1939) also comment constructively upon

TABLE 5. Characteristics of the Various Strains of *Malbranchea*.

Strain	Pathogenicity	Color	Measurements (μ) Hyphae	Spores
Mesophiles[a]				
Bolognesi and Chiurco 1925	+	Rose	0.7–1.2	2.5–5.2
Kambayashi 1934	+	Yellow to brown	1.5 — 2.5	3–5.5 × 2–4.5
Rivelloni 1937	±	Yellow, rose, brown	—	6.5–7.5 × 3–4
Buisman 193?	Unknown	Pale yellow or rose	—	2.5–3 × 2
Elisei 1940	Unknown	Yellow or rose	0.5–4	2–10 × 1.5–2.5
Thermophiles[b]				
Miehe 1907	Unknown	Yellow to brown	Up to 5	2.5–10 × 2.5–3
Crisan 1959	Unknown	Yellow to tan	2.5–3	3.5–6 × 3–4
Our #27	—[c]	Yellow to reddish brown	Up to 4	3–7 × 3–4.5
Temperature Relations Unknown				
Saccardo and Penzig 1882	Unknown	Yellow	0.5–2	3 × 2.5

[a] Growth at 20°C but none at 40°C.
[b] Growth at 50°C but none at 20°C.
[c] Dr. C. W. Emmons reported to us (letter April 3, 1947) that so far as he could determine from animal inoculations our strain #27 from retting guayule was not pathogenic.

the unusual mode of spore formation in *Malbranchea* and its significance in establishing natural relationships. They credit Kambayashi (1934) with a proper appreciation of the alternating thick-walled spores and sterile, thin-walled isthmuses, whereas it is evident that Miehe (1907b) had really made this quite clear many years before. They point out that while the spores do develop a secondary wall within the initial hyphal wall and can in that sense be considered as endospores, they are not true endoconidia because they are never released from the hyphal "sleeve." Their release, on the contrary, is brought about by the disintegration of the thin-walled isthmuses, and since this disarticulation occurs quite a time after septation of the fertile hyphae, spore formation in *Malbranchea* must also be distinguished from arthrospore formation in such genera as *Geotrichum* where there are no cellular isthmuses and spore disarticulation is almost simultaneous with hyphal septation. They also conclude that, despite a general similarity between the coiled fertile hyphae of *Malbranchea* and the coiled conidia of the Helicosporeae, the analogy is only a superficial one, for in reality the two methods of spore formation are basically very different.

Elisei (1940) enters into a complex account of spore formation, enumerating several additional types of spores neither seen by us nor reported by other workers. Unfortunately, our efforts to clarify this aspect have been unsuccessful thus far. The Rivelloni strain of *Malbranchea* that we recently obtained from the Centraalbureau voor Schimmelcultures at Baarn, as an example of the mesophilic forms which Elisei was considering, is entirely white and mycelial, apparently having lost in serial transfer the capacity for normal spore production. We can only surmise that Elisei's other spore types may be unusual departures from the basic pattern of pseudo-endospore formation now so well established in *Malbranchea*.

With its unicellular, light-colored conidia, *Malbranchea* would fall in the Moniliaceae as defined by Clements and Shear (1931). Hughes (1953) has recently stressed the nature and mode of formation of conidia as a guide to natural relationships within the Fungi Imperfecti. According to his scheme, *Malbranchea* would be included in Group VII, where (p. 640) "conidia arise from the septation and breaking up of simple or branched hyphae" or, in other words (p. 581), conidia develop "by the basipetal fragmentation of conidiophores of determinate length, and which do not possess a meristematic zone." Hughes recognizes within this type two different subtypes. In one, illustrated by *Geotrichum*, all cells in the chain become spores; in the other, alternate cells remain sterile and thin-walled and ultimately serve as disjunctors. He cites the genus *Coremiella* as an example of this second subtype, and from his figures and description it is evident that *Malbranchea* produces its conidia in essentially this same fashion. He says (p. 640): "The intermediate cells lose their contents entirely and the lateral walls remain thin, collapse inwards, and finally break readily to free the oblong or cuboidal conidia. The conidium it will be realized has developed within the outer wall of the original hypha and the characteristic papilla and minute pore of the end wall are clearly visible: conidia which have seceded show a minute frill at each end, this being the remains of the outer wall of the original hypha belonging to one of the collapsed cells." We have not detected a pore in the end wall of our spores, and of course there are numerous other differences between *Malbranchea* and *Coremiella*, but it is nevertheless most interesting to see how closely the method of conidium formation agrees in the two genera.

Diagnosis

Hyphae colorless at first, later yellow, 1.5–4.5 μ in diameter; fertile hyphae irregularly septate near the base with conspicuous swellings proximal to the septations, 3–4 μ in diameter; swellings up to 10 μ in diameter; terminal portion 2.0–2.6 μ in diameter, regularly branched, the branches arising at right angles to the supporting hyphae, at first nonseptate, later becoming regularly septate and forming blocklike cells from the apex toward the base; alternate cells, or occasionally alternate groups of cells, becoming thick-walled spores separated by thin-walled, sterile cells which soon die and collapse; spores pale yellow or colorless, subcylindrical, often slightly curved or irregular, 3–7 × 3–4.5 μ.

Malbranchea pulchella Saccardo and Penzig var. *sulfurea* (Miehe) n. comb.

Distinguished from the type by its temperature characteristics: minimum, about 25°C; optimum, about 45°C; and maximum, about 55°C. A varietate typica notis temperietris: minimo ca. 25°C, optimo ca. 45°C, ac maximo ca. 55°C, distinguitur.

Represented by specimen M206518 in the University of California Herbarium, Berkeley (our culture #27).

Temperature Relations

Miehe (1907b) included in his original description a very precise statement of the temperature characteristics of *Malbranchea pulchella* var. *sulfurea*. He said that growth was very slow at 26° and 27.5°C, better but still slow at 30°C, starting to be rapid at 35°C, still good at 50°C but failing to form spores, and ceasing altogether at about 53°C. We have little to add. Our records show minimum between 26° and 28°C, optimum about 45°C, and maximum between 55°C and 57°C. Crisan (1959) listed 29–30°, 45–46°, and 53°C as the cardinal temperatures he observed for this species. It is distinctly thermophilic but not quite as markedly so as a few of the others, such as *Humicola lanuginosa*.

12

SPOROTRICHUM THERMOPHILE

Sporotrichum Link ex Fries (1832, pp. 415–416)

Sporotrichum thermophile Apinis (1963a)

Occurrence

The existence of a thermophilic species of *Sporotrichum* was first brought to our attention by the work of Dr. Aino Henssen. In her investigations (1957b) on the decomposition of stable manure by microorganisms, she examined and later isolated three thermophilic fungi. We were able to obtain and study two of her three isolates. These were sent to us from Berlin, Germany, by Dr. Bortels, Director, Biologische Bundesanstalt. One of these isolates (R 29) proved to be identical to our *Humicola insolens*, while the other (R 81) was obviously *Humicola lanuginosa*. Dr. Bortels informed us that the third isolate (R 38), which Henssen refers to as *Sporotrichum* sp., was not viable. We were, therefore, unable to study this organism firsthand. The characteristics of *Sporotrichum* sp., as listed below, represent Henssen's observations of this organism.

Morphology and Cultural Characteristics

Henssen reports the *Sporotrichum* sp. was first obtained from stable manure and was subsequently isolated in pure culture on pectin agar. It also grew well on potato agar and on glucose-peptone agar. On the latter medium, orange to red-brown pigments were produced. On nutrient agar, with pure cellulose as the carbon source, growth was weaker. Henssen (1957b, p. 68) figures the hyphae and conidia of her isolate and describes their characteristics briefly as follows: hyphae colorless, about 2 μ broad; conidia colorless, oval or pyriform, 4–8 × 2–4(5) μ.

Taxonomy

Subsequent to Henssen's isolation of *Sporotrichum* sp., a similar thermophilic *Sporotrichum* was described by Apinis (1963a) to which he gave the name S. *thermophile*. His isolate, which he obtained several times from soil collected near Attenborough, England, appears to be identical to the organism Henssen described simply as *Sporotrichum* sp. Therefore, we are accepting the name S. *thermophile*, as proposed by Apinis, to include Henssen's isolate. The reader is referred to Apinis' paper (1963a) for figures of this species.

Temperature Relations

Sporotrichum thermophile grew most rapidly at temperatures between 40° and 50°C. At 28°C the organism grew more slowly, and at 55°C no growth was observed. These temperature figures are, as were the preceding morphological and cultural characteristics, those reported by Henssen. Apinis (1963a) states that his isolate grew quite rapidly on most agar media at 38°C. On Czapek's agar most rapid growth occurred at 28–29°C, and no growth was observed at 47–48°C. Evidently Apinis' fungus was not quite as thermophilic as Henssen's. In any event, the species is very near the limit of our definition of a true thermophile.

13

EXCLUDED OR DOUBTFUL THERMOPHILES

In this section we will discuss briefly a number of organisms that cannot, on the basis of present information, take a secure place among the known thermophilic fungi. In some instances this exclusion is based simply upon the arbitrary definition of thermophile that we have adopted (see §1). We are not concerned here with the many fungi that Jourde (1908) and other early workers termed thermophilic simply because they had maxima between 40° and 45°C. Furthermore, though a fungus may thrive at temperatures above 45°C, we do not consider it to be thermophilic if it also can continue vigorous growth at temperatures below 20°C. Such a fungus is *Aspergillus fumigatus*, which Miehe (1907a) and others have included in the category psychrotolerant because it readily tolerates temperatures below 20°C even though its maximum is 50°C or slightly higher. Certain species of the Mucorales [such as *Mucor corymbifer* Cohn = *Absidia lichtheimii* (Lucet and Costantin) Lendner and *Absidia ramosa* (Lindt) Lendner] and a number of other fungi would also be placed in this category. Much has been written about them because of their participation in microbial thermogenesis, their implication in various diseases of warm-blooded animals, their frequent occurrence in natural fermentations, and their general biological interest. We have not included them in this account.

More difficult to deal with and hence requiring somewhat further consideration are borderline cases or descriptions that do not provide sufficiently precise information to permit a clear-cut decision to be reached. Several such cases will be considered in the following paragraphs.

Micromucor naumovii Mal'chevskaya (1939, p. 25)
? = *Mortierella* sp.

One of the several fungi isolated from self-heated peat by Mal'chevskaya (1939) was given the binomial *Micromucor naumovii*. *Micromucor* is not recognized as a generic name by Zycha (1935), Hesseltine (1955), or Ainsworth (1961). It is apparently only a sectional designation within the genus *Mucor* as presented by Naumov (1935). At all events, the fungus in question was described as producing a white felt composed of septate hyphae 5.2–6.9 μ wide, which sometimes formed yellowish chlamydospores 10–12 μ in diameter. Sporangia were grayish yellow, 13.8–17.3 μ in diameter, and produced oval spores 2.0×1.7 μ. Mal'chevskaya's Fig. 2 shows several sporangiophores and sporangia, with no suggestion of columellae but with pronounced septations in the sporangiophores and a distinctive swelling at the base. To the best of our knowledge there are no species of *Mucor* with sporangiospores as small as those described here. Because of the apparent lack of a columella and the occurrence of such small spores, as well as swollen regions subtending the sporangiophores, this organism might more properly be placed in the genus *Mortierella*. Indeed, it appears very similar to *Mortierella turficola* Ling-Young (1930). Mal'chevskaya reported that it grew well at 25–30°C and 40–50°C, so we have no positive evidence of its thermophilic nature. One can only say that we should be alert to the possible occurrence of a thermophilic, mucoraceous fungus of this sort, probably belonging to the genus *Mortierella*.

Yeasts and Yeastlike Fungi

There appear to be no well-established instances of real thermophilism among the true yeasts (Endomycetales). There is no reference to thermophiles in the book by Arima et al. (1957), and they are accorded only brief mention in the volume prepared by Cook (1958).

The species *Saccharomyces thermantitonum* was described by Johnson (1905). It was apparently quite similar to *S. cerevisiae* in morphology but had an optimum temperature between 40° and 45°C and a maximum near 50°C. It also grew at 25°C but much more slowly. Subsequent workers, however, were all unable fifteen years later to verify the high-temperature characteristics of various subcultures of this original isolate (Euler and

Laurin, 1920; and compare, Lodder and Kreger-van Rij, 1952, p. 169). They suggested that its new characteristics (maximum below 38°C) might be due to adaptation over a long period of subculturing at 16–20°C. That stocks were kept at such temperatures is enough by itself to suggest that S. *thermantitonum*, even in its original form, would not meet our criteria for thermophilism. Lodder and Kreger-van Rij (1952) classify it as *Saccharomyces willianus*.

Nor is there any evidence that the S. *cerevisiae* strain *thermophilus* mentioned by Lodder and Kreger-van Rij (1952) was anything other than a thermotolerant form.

Of considerable interest is the organism *Saccharomycopsis guttulata*, investigated recently by Shifrine and Phaff (1958). This ascosporic yeast, which will grow only within the narrow temperature range of 35° to 40°C, occurs normally in the gastrointestinal tract of rabbits. Even though it has evidently become specially adapted to its life in a warm-blooded animal, it still does not come under our particular definition of thermophilic fungi.

Another yeast or yeastlike fungus was described in detail by Odintsova (1947), who named it *Endoblastomyces thermophilus* nov. gen., nov. sp. This work is discussed at length by Mishustin (1950) but must have been overlooked by yeast investigators as well as mycologists in general because there is no mention of it in either Lodder and Kreger-van Rij (1952) or Ainsworth's (1961) *Dictionary of the Fungi*. Morphologically, *E. thermophilus*, which apparently forms true mycelium—as well as pseudomycelium, arthrospores, and blastospores—could probably be included in *Trichosporon* Behrend. The name *Endoblastomyces* was based, however, upon the peculiar endogenous formation of small yeast cells within the larger cells of mycelium or pseudomycelium. At all events this fungus, which was derived from an enrichment culture of lactic acid bacteria in a bread factory in Central Asia, was considered by Odintsova (1947) and Mishustin (1950) to be thermophilic. In mixed culture with certain bacteria it grew at 48°C, but in pure culture its maximum was only 44°C. It apparently grew well at 20°C, and we can designate it, like *Saccharomyces thermantitonum*, as mildly thermotolerant rather than thermophilic.

Regarding thermophilism in the yeasts, Ingram (p. 613 in Cook, 1958) sums up the evidence by saying: "Various yeasts have been described as thermophilic, but none of the supposedly thermophilic strains which have fallen into the writer's hands have been really unusual in this respect." Indeed, thus far, no yeasts have been described that clearly satisfy our definition of thermophily in the fungi.

Oidium-Oospora

In his studies of self-heating hay, Miehe (1907a) examined in detail isolates of what he called *Oidium lactis* Fresenius, which is properly designated as *Oospora lactis* (Fresenius) Saccardo or, according to a recent interpretation by Carmichael (1957), *Geotrichum candidum* Link ex Persoon. Miehe found this fungus, sometimes in great quantities, on old dried hay that had been dampened, but it was not a major part of the flora of freshly wilted, self-heating hay. He considered it important only in the early stages of microbial thermogenesis and reported that it grew well at 35°C but not at all at 40°C. It grows vigorously at 20°C and is in no sense thermophilic.

Oidium was also mentioned in the papers by Waksman and his colleagues on the composting of manure and plant residues. They stated (Waksman, Cordon, and Hulpoi, 1939) that at 50°C "the fungi were largely represented by the *Thermomyces* and the *Monilia* or *Oidium* groups." Insufficient information is provided to allow more precise identification of these forms. No doubt *Thermomyces lanuginosus* was well represented, but it seems unlikely that members of the genus *Oospora* were active at 50°C. Possibly some of the monilioid forms seen by Waksman et al. are referable to the genus *Torula* (see §10).

Penicillium sp.

In his later studies of thermogenesis in pure cultures, Miehe (1930a, pp. 96–97) gave an account of a fungus which he ascribed to the genus *Penicillium*. He reported that in attempting to reisolate *Thermoascus*, which had been lost in the interval since their earlier work, Dr. Maeckel isolated a similar fungus with temperature characteristics much like those of *Thermoascus aurantiacus*. Its limits for growth were approximately 35°C minimum and 60°C maximum. Clearly it was a genuine thermophile. However, its morphological characteristics were not presented in sufficient detail to permit definite identification. It was described as having limited conidium production and a profuse perfect stage represented by round, orange-yellow perithecia that covered the agar in a mealy yellow layer. No figures or measurements were given and, to our knowledge, no further information was ever published on this isolate. Possibly it represents another species of *Thermoascus*, or it could be a second thermophilic *Penicillium*.

We have insufficient data for any decision, and Miehe never applied a specific epithet to it.

Species Referable to the Genus *Paecilomyces*

In their monographs, Thom (1930) and Raper and Thom (1949) have discussed a number of fungi that are capable of growing vigorously at temperatures between 40° and 50°C and that, although assigned to diverse genera by their authors, can be grouped together in the genus *Paecilomyces*. Of special interest to us is *Penicillium arenarium* Shaposhnikov and Manteifel (1923), which was discovered by these Russian workers during their investigations of the microflora of acidic fermentations. They report that it appeared at a temperature of about 40°C in a chamber where the level of atmospheric oxygen had been reduced with pyrogallol. From their extensive investigation of the morphology and physiology of *P. arenarium*, we can summarize the major characteristics. In pure culture on a wide variety of artificial media the mycelium was always white at first and then changed usually to some shade of sandy olive. The name *arenarium* (L. *arena*, sand) was selected because of this sandy color, and the authors frequently referred to it as the sand mold. On certain media, however, more pronounced greenish or even bluish hues were developed. The reverse ranged from white or light yellow to dark brown. Scattered overgrowths of white hyphae occurred and more compacted masses of mycelium, 3–4 mm in diameter, were noted. The possibility was considered that the latter structures might be incipient ascocarps but no real evidence of a perfect stage was presented. Conidiophores arose as short side branches up to 150 μ long by 5–6 μ broad. The conidial apparatus was of the penicillium type but very irregular, with metulae of variable size and arrangement. Phialides were large, 25 μ or more in length by 5–6 μ broad, flask-shaped and strongly acuminate. Large, lemon-shaped conidia, 6–11 × 3.5–6 μ, were borne in chains. Thick-walled gemmae, 14–15 μ in diameter, were also formed on side branches of the mycelium. Under certain conditions coremia sometimes developed but they were usually sterile. The fungus was reported to be particularly resistant to high levels of citric acid and tannins. Its temperature characteristics were: minimum, about 20°C (room temperature); optimum, 35–40°C; and maximum, 48°C.

So far as we have been able to determine, no one has recognized this particular fungus again since its first description by Shaposhnikov and Manteifel. Thom (1930) considered it to be in the *Paecilomyces varioti* series and Raper and Thom (1949) referred to it as a thermophile. According to our criteria, however, it is just on the borderline. As we have not had an opportunity to examine it ourselves, and since its maximum is only slightly over 45°C, we prefer not to include it among the well-defined thermophiles.

Another fungus belonging to this general assemblage is *Corollium dermatophagum*, found on an old pair of army boots in Norway and described by Sopp in 1912. Here again we have a penicillium-like mold with yellow-green or light brown growth and very irregularly placed sterigmata. Again Raper and Thom (1949) consider it to be *Paecilomyces* and state that it is thermophilic. According to Sopp's description, however, *C. dermatophagum*, although growing even somewhat above 45°C and having an optimum at 38–40°C, still grows well much below 20°C. Quite clearly it is in our category of thermotolerant forms.

Our own strain of *Paecilomyces varioti* (#R16) from retting guayule merits brief mention here. It was isolated by W. A. Campbell and identified in K. B. Raper's laboratory at Peoria in 1944. Its temperature characteristics are much like those of the isolates from Norway and Russia discussed just above—namely, a maximum of 47°C and a minimum of 10°C, with excellent growth occurring between 20° and 40°C. It too, we would consider thermotolerant rather than thermophilic.

But it cannot be overlooked that the imperfect stage of *Thermoascus aurantiacus* itself bears a marked resemblance to *Paecilomyces*. Perhaps there is a range of temperature characteristics as well as sexual expression in this genus. Clearly there is a need for closer comparative investigation of the temperature relations and reproductive behavior of a whole series of fungi exhibiting the general morphological features of the genus *Paecilomyces*. The reader is referred to the recent study of *Paecilomyces* by Brown and Smith (1957), which emphasizes the relation to *Byssochlamys* but is not specifically concerned with temperature limits. (See also Addenda.)

Agaricaceae—*Coprinus*

There are a few records of Agaricaceae occurring at quite high temperatures. All these records appear to concern *Coprinus*, a genus which is not infrequently associated with manure piles, compost heaps, or other masses of self-heating plant materials. In connection with his work on fungal decomposition of cellulose, Rege (1927) isolated a species which he said most closely resembled *C. fimetarius* Fries. The mycelium grew between the temperatures of 14° and 46°C and showed an optimum at 30–35°C.

Soon after, Perrier (1929) isolated from self-heated stable manure another *Coprinus*, possibly *C. stercorarius*. He demonstrated that the mycelium could tolerate a temperature of 55–57°C for six weeks, but he did not establish the upper or lower limits for growth. Reese (1946), studying aerobic decomposition of cellulose by microorganisms at temperatures above 40°C, again isolated a *Coprinus*, which he designated simply as *Coprinus* sp. It was reported to have a rather high optimum temperature for growth, around 45°C, but it would not grow above 55°C. Presumably it grew perfectly well at temperatures near 20°C or below.

We too were impressed by the appearance of numerous sporophores of a *Coprinus* on the surface of large stationary rets of guayule shrub in which marked heating had occurred. In one instance the shrub was cut to one half-inch particles and retted in a bin; in another instance whole shrub had been retted in the bale, with the leaves still attached. Material from the former ret was examined at the Herbarium of the University of California, Berkeley, and identified by Mrs. Vera M. Miller as *C. lagopus*. We made no isolations of this material from guayule and so have no precise information regarding its temperature characteristics. The limited evidence at hand, therefore, suggests that although some members of the genus *Coprinus* grow at temperatures between 45° and 55°C, none is truly thermophilic. However, a systematic study of temperature relations in the Agaricaceae, and especially among the species of *Coprinus*, may well reveal that thermophilism does indeed occur in this group.

This is an appropriate point to consider Špaček's two papers (1953, 1954), whose Czech title is "Studie o teplobytné mykofloře moravské." Špaček himself gives as a German rendition of his title "Thermophile Mycoflora in Mähren," which, in English, becomes "Moravian thermophilic mycoflora." That the papers have in fact nothing to do with thermophily in the accepted microbiological sense was established by examination of their detailed German summaries. The work deals with the agaricaceous flora that occurs in certain xerothermic (warm, dry) areas of Southern Europe. According to Dr. Emil Kovtun, the Czechoslovakian word *teplobytné* is to be translated as warm-living or warm-inhabiting rather than warmth-loving. We are pointing this out here lest some future student be led to believe, as we did, that Špaček's papers contain special information on thermophilic fungi.

This concludes our account of the fungi which, from a cursory examination of the literature, might be thought to come under the category of thermophiles. In each case, we consider that the present evidence shows they are not really thermophilic, or it is insufficient to establish their true systematic position or their thermophilism or both. We can not claim to have made an exhaustive search in the literature for all references to thermophilic fungi. However, we believe that each such reference should be submitted to the kind of critical analysis we have presented here so that a true and complete picture of the existing thermophilic mold flora will emerge.

14

DIAGNOSTIC KEY TO THE THERMOPHILIC FUNGI*

PHYCOMYCETES

I. Terrestrial fungi with generally nonseptate hyphae; asexual reproduction by aplanospores borne in terminal sporangia; sexual reproduction by means of zygospores .... Order MUCORALES
   A. Fungus heterothallic .... *Mucor pusillus*
   B. Fungus homothallic .... *Mucor miehei*

ASCOMYCETES

I. Ascocarp a true cleistothecium lacking an ostiole; asci scattered within the ascocarp .... Order EUROTIALES
   A. Cleistothecia rare; ascospores with distinct equatorial ridges; conidiophores minute .... *Talaromyces (Penicillium) duponti*
   B. Cleistothecia common; ascospores smooth, minutely pitted but lacking equatorial ridges; conidiophores large
   Thermoascus aurantiacus
II. Ascocarp a perithecium with a definite ostiole, or a perithecium-like stroma lacking a definite ostiole
   A. Ascocarp a perithecium; asci arranged in a basal tuft in the ascocarp .... Order SPHAERIALES
   Perithecia superficial; terminal hairs dichotomously branched; asci cylindrical, 8-spored, unistichous .... *Chaetomium thermophile*
   1. Perithecia gregarious
      a. Dichotomously branched hairs limited to the upper portion of the perithecium .... *C. thermophile* var. *thermophile*

---

* See Addenda also.

   b. Dichotomously branched hairs more or less covering the
    entire perithecium .... *C. thermophile* var. *coprophile*
  2. Perithecia scattered, only occasionally gregarious
             C. thermophile var. *dissitum*
 B. Ascocarp a perithecium-like stroma lacking a definite ostiole; asci
  arranged in one or more tufts in the center of the ascocarp
           Order PSEUDOSPHAERIALES
  Ascocarp spherical, superficial, glabrous; asci 8-spored, unitunicate .... *Myriococcum albomyces*

FUNGI IMPERFECTI (DEUTEROMYCETES)

I. Spores not produced within a pycnidium or acervulus
               Order MONILIALES
 A. Spores, and often the hyphae, brown or dark brown
  1. Spores typically borne singly or in short chains on short, lateral
   aleuriophores
   a. Aleuriospores smooth-walled; dark intercalary spores
    present
    1. Spores usually borne singly on lateral aleuriophores; in-
     tercalary spores not common
             Humicola grisea var. *thermoidea*
    2. Spores borne singly or in short chains; globose and
     spindle-shaped intercalary spores common
                Humicola insolens
   b. Aleuriospores with irregular or sculptured walls; dark inter-
    calary spores lacking
    1. Aleuriospores globose, exospore irregularly sculptured
                Humicola lanuginosa
    2. Aleuriospores stellate .... *Humicola stellata*
  2. Spores produced only in chains, either intercalarily in the main
   and branch hyphae or developed basipetally on side branches
               Torula thermophila
 B. Spores and hyphae colorless or bright colored
  1. Spores produced intercalarily in the coiled apical portions of
   septate, fertile, hyphal branches, the spores usually separated
   from one another by sterile cells
          Malbranchea pulchella var. *sulfurea*
  2. Spores attached apically and laterally near the tip of an irregularly branched conidiophore *Sporotrichum thermophile*

PART III

General Biology and Practical Importance of Thermophilic Fungi

15

SYSTEMATIC DISTRIBUTION, TEMPERATURE RELATIONS, AND NATURAL OCCURRENCE

Phylogeny and Taxonomy of Thermophiles

There is no indication that thermophilism is more strongly developed in any one of the three classes of fungi represented—Phycomycetes, Ascomycetes, and Fungi Imperfecti—than in the others. As we have noted before, the Basidiomycetes are conspicuous by their absence, but members of this fourth class may well be added to the group ultimately. The phylogenetic heterogeneity that characterizes the thermophilic fungi (see Fig. 67) makes it virtually certain that thermophilism arose repeatedly among different genera of Eumycota. It seems likely to us too that present-day thermophiles were derived from mesophilic ancestors, a conclusion also reached by Mishustin (1950). This idea is, we believe, further borne out by the lack of any sharp line between mesophiles and thermophiles. Each group grades very gradually into the other. We agree with Vouk (1929) that thermophilic microorganisms are not relics of early life on earth, and we find unconvincing Copeland's (1936) proposal that many mesophiles were derived from thermophilic ancestors. At the present time, however, it must be admitted that there is no very concrete evidence upon which to base any definite conclusions regarding phylogeny of the thermophilic fungi.

Various aspects of the taxonomy of the thermophilic fungi remain to be worked out. The difficulty encountered in properly classifying a number of the species and varieties, especially those in the Fungi Imperfecti, is evidence that the genera involved are in need of revision. However, the

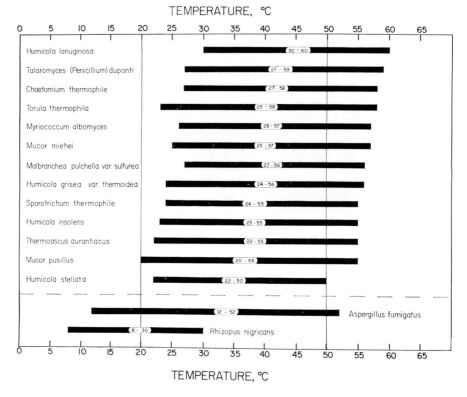

Fig. 67.
Minimum and maximum temperatures for growth of the thermophilic Eumycota. Data for *Rhizopus nigricans,* a common mesophile, and *Aspergillus fumigatus,* one of the most thermotolerant mesophiles, were obtained with isolates derived from retting guayule and are included here for comparison.

number of known thermophiles is still so small that, once their thermophilic character has been established, it will be a relatively easy matter, even for nonspecialists, to identify future isolates by means of the simple key we have provided (§14). Hence recognition of already described taxa will be facilitated and any newly discovered species can be definitively added to the group.

Temperature Relations Compared

Inasmuch as our entire report is based upon the unusual temperature characteristics of the thermophilic fungi, a brief comparison of their various temperature relations will serve at this point as an effective summary. The data are graphically presented in Figure 67. As we emphasized in §1, our definition of thermophilism is necessarily arbitrary, and the lowest of the thermophiles, *Humicola stellata*, is but slightly removed from the highest of the thermotolerant mesophiles such as *Aspergillus fumigatus*. Indeed the latter has a slightly higher maximum, but it is excluded from the thermophilic category because it grows at temperatures well below 20°C. The failure to grow below 20°C, even more than the capacity to grow at or above 50°C, may be considered the real hallmark of the thermophile. This matter will be referred to again in §19. It is interesting to observe that the entire range of fungal thermophilism is spanned by the species of *Humicola*, with *H. stellata* at the bottom, *H. insolens* and *H. grisea* var. *thermoidea* about midway, and *H. lanuginosa* at the very top.

At the present time we cannot say why the top limit of growth for fungi is 60°C, neither appreciably lower, as it is for animals, nor much higher, as it is for bacteria, Actinomycetes, and blue-green algae (compare §1). Possibly the less highly evolved subcellular architecture of the latter three groups of microorganisms is involved in their normal development at the highest temperatures. We really do not know. Certain proposed mechanisms to account for thermophilism will be considered below.

In closing this brief comparison of temperature relations one further matter requires particular emphasis. Doubtless there are other interesting thermophilic Eumycota to be discovered, and new efforts will certainly be made to find them in the future. In carrying out these explorations, it cannot be stressed too strongly that the key to successful isolation is the temperature of incubation. Temperatures of 45° or 50°C provide, in the simplest manner, an environment that inhibits the vast numbers of mesophilic fungi while favoring and hence, as the bacteriologists say, enriching the thermophilic ones. This is such a self-evident point that it could be considered elementary. There are, however, modern studies of the microbiology of self-heating organic materials in which this very point appears to be entirely overlooked. Christensen (1946) and Christensen and Gordon (1948), for example, in their quantitative evaluations of the mold flora of stored grain and flour and its possible significance in self-heating (see §17), were careful to use appropriate media and sampling procedures but, so far as we can see, never incubated their cultures at temperatures higher than 25°C. Understandably, not one of the thermophilic fungi was recognized. More recently, in extensive investigations of the fungi in self-heated fodder, Müller (1961a) incubated his cultures at 25° and 37°C. It is not surprising, therefore, that, although numerous common mesophilic molds were found

(Müller, 1961a and 1961b), no true thermophilic fungi were isolated from these fodder preparations, which regularly heated to 60°C. Unquestionably, thermophiles were present and played an important role in the fodder processing, but even at 37°C they were crowded out by mesophilic species in the isolation plates. Even Crisan (1959) failed to take full advantage of the "heat-loving" characteristics of the organisms he was seeking by incubating many of his initial isolation cultures at 40°C rather than 45°C or higher. In attempting to enrich for thermophilic fungi, appropriately high incubation temperatures are essential.

Sources of the Known Species

The early discoveries of thermophilic fungi were made in continental Europe in the late nineteenth and early twentieth centuries—in France, Germany, and Italy. This, of course, is simply a reflection of the distribution of scientific centers and research interests at that time and is no indication of the geographical distribution of thermophilic fungi. After Hagem (1908) found *Mucor pusillus* and Sopp (1912) discovered *Thermoascus*, both in Norway, little additional knowledge about the natural distribution of these fungi was gained for some years. In 1927 Rege isolated from composts in England what he called *Acremoniella* sp. but was almost certainly *Humicola lanuginosa*, and Nielsen (1927) in that same year listed *Mucor pusillus* among the fungi obtained from soil from North Greenland. Soon after, Lendner (1929) reported a culture of *Mucor pusillus* (his *M. Buntingii*) derived from fermenting cacao seeds in the African Gold Coast. Otani (1931) subsequently published his work on the temperature relations of various species of *Mucor* and among these was *M. pusillus*. Unfortunately we have not succeeded thus far in our effort to determine the precise source of Otani's strain. Apparently many of his isolates came originally from China, Taiwan, or other parts of the Orient. Somewhat later, the Russian workers (Isachenko and Mal'chevskaya, 1936; Mal'chevskaya, 1939) found *Thermoascus aurantiacus*—and probably *Talaromyces* (*Penicillium*) *duponti* as well—on self-heating piles of peat. By 1939 Waksman and his co-workers (Waksman and Cordon, 1939; Waksman, Cordon, and Hulpoi, 1939; Waksman, Umbreit, and Cordon, 1939) were studying thermophilic species of *Humicola* on composting materials in the eastern United States. This appears to be the first recognized discovery of a truly thermophilic fungus in the western hemisphere. Within a few years Diehl (personal communication) had found *Malbranchea pulchella* var. *sulfurea* in leaf compost in Washington, D.C., Rode et al. (1947) had isolated it from manure compost in Texas, and we ourselves had made extensive collections and isolations of numerous thermophilic fungi from guayule and other substrata in California. Crisan (1959) subsequently made many other collections in Indiana and Pennsylvania. Henssen (1957b) had, meanwhile, found *Humicola lanuginosa* and *H. insolens* in Finland as well as Germany. Thus there is ample evidence that the thermophilic molds, like their mesophilic counterparts, are probably essentially world-wide in their distribution and will be found wherever they are sought for in their normal environment and by the proper methods. (See Addenda.)

As to their normal or natural environment, Table 6 is a sufficiently complete representation of collection data to establish a number of points with reasonable certainty. Miehe (1907a, Kap. IX, Die thermophilen Mikroorganismen und ihre Existenzbedingungen in der Natur) clearly understood that the most significant natural sites for the growth and reproduction of the saprophytic, thermophilic microorganisms are those masses of decomposing organic matter in which microbial thermogenesis (see below) itself produces the heat required to raise the material to temperatures favoring the thermophiles. Two physicochemical requirements must be met: the material must have sufficient readily available nutrient (usually fairly soluble carbohydrates and some amino acids) to support vigorous microbial metabolism, and it must be in a sufficiently large and compact mass to be reasonably well self-insulated. It must, besides, be porous enough to allow aerobic metabolism. Thus it is quite understandable that Miehe's pioneering studies of self-heating hay revealed such a large number of important high-temperature microorganisms and that our own investigations of retting guayule permitted us to isolate the first group of thermophilic fungi upon which the present study is based. Indeed, Table 6 shows that of the 15 fungi listed 9 were derived from hay and/or guayule; if the composts and leaf mold are included, all but one of the known thermophilic fungi are represented. The isolations from mushroom compost were made by investigators at the Butler County Mushroom Farm in Pennsylvania and were sent to us for identification in 1953: 30 were *Humicola grisea* var. *thermoidea*, 15 were *Humicola lanuginosa*, 11 were *Torula thermophila*, and 1 proved to be *Myriococcum albomyces*. Noteworthy also are the isolations of *Talaromyces* and *Thermoascus* from self-heated peat (Isachenko and Mal'chevskaya, 1936; Mal'chevskaya, 1939).

Haymows, guayule rets, garden composts, and manure piles are all man-

TABLE 6. The Natural Occurrence of the Thermophilic Eumycota.

(Some isolations were made directly from the substratum but most of the material was first incubated in the laboratory at an elevated temperature to develop the thermophilic flora.)

Isolates	Substrates						
	Microbially Self-heated Materials						
	Guayule Rets	Hay and Grass	Garden Compost	Manure	Leaf Mold	Mushroom Compost	Peat
Mucor pusillus	+	+[a]			+		
Mucor miehei	+	+					
Talaromyces (Penicillium) duponti	+	+	+	+			+[b]
Thermoascus aurantiacus	+	+	+				+
Myriococcum albomyces						+	
Chaetomium thermophile var. thermophile			+				
var. dissitum					+		
var. coprophile		+					
Humicola insolens	+			+			
Humicola grisea var. thermoidea			+			+	
Humicola lanuginosa	+	+	+	+	+	+	
Humicola stellata		+					
Torula thermophila						+	
Malbranchea pulchella var. sulfurea	+	+		+	+		
Sporotrichum sp.							

SOURCE: Data for this table were derived from our own work as well as literature referred to in the text. Also see Addenda.

[a] Since Miehe's (1907a) isolates from hay produced zygospores regularly, they were probably *M. miehei*, but very possibly *M. pusillus* was also represented. Noack (1912) and others undoubtedly also isolated *M. pusillus* from grass or hay.

[b] It is not possible to be certain about the identity of this isolate from peat reported by Mal'chevskaya (1939). (See text.)

TABLE 6. (*continued*)

Isolates	Substrates			
	Other Materials			
	Herbivore Dung	Various Plant Substances	Nesting Materials	Living Animals
Mucor pusillus	Horse	Cacao seeds,[c] bread, and gas mask		Dog, cow, pig, fowl, and horse
Mucor miehei	Horse			Calf brain[d]
Talaromyces (*Penicillium*) *duponti*		Straw		
Thermoascus aurantiacus		Wood and cacao husks		
Myriococcum albomyces			Chicken nest, straw	
Chaetomium thermophile var. *thermophile*		Straw		
var. *dissitum*			Coot nest, Typha	
var. *coprophile*	Horse, cow, rabbit, and goat	Straw	Blackbird nest, twigs	
Humicola insolens	Cow and sheep			
Humicola grisea var. *thermoidea*	Elephant			
Humicola lanuginosa	Horse, sheep, and pig	Potato,[e] oats, straw, and grain		Cow
Humicola stellata				
Torula thermophila	Horse		Chicken nest, straw	
Malbranchea pulchella var. *sulfurea*	Goat	Cardboard and cordage		
Sporotrichum sp.	Mixed			

[c] Zycha (1935, p. 52) said that Lendner's (1929) *M. pusillus* had come from piled coconuts (Kokosnussen) in the Gold Coast but Lendner (1929, p. 261) said cacao seeds piled for fermentation (semences de cacao)!

[d] It is not entirely clear, in Smith's (1957) account of the zygosporic *Mucor*, precisely which of Ainsworth and Austwick's (1955) isolates he was studying.

[e] Inoculated with garden soil. Tsiklinskaya (1899, p. 504) says: "Le mycelium du champignon fut remarque sur une pomme ensemencée avec des parcelles de terre du jardin." As did Miehe (1907a), we presume Tsiklinskaya's "pomme" was a potato, since she used that substratum for other isolations.

made, and one might rightly question their being recorded as natural sites. However, everyone is familiar with the ways that organic waste materials become piled in windrows by the natural forces of wind and water. Both Miehe (1907a) and Noack (1912) considered this matter carefully and concluded that there certainly must be in nature many situations where natural microbial thermogenesis, coupled with insulation, would lead to temperatures favoring the development of thermophiles. It must be admitted that neither they nor we—nor others, so far as we are aware—have ever reported temperatures in the range of 40° or 50°C in naturally piled organic debris heated solely by microbial activity.

There are, however, several other natural sources of heat that Miehe (1907a) and Noack (1912) also considered. Possibly the most significant is insolation. Sames (1900), for example, demonstrated many years ago that temperatures of 40–50°C or more are reached in surface soils during the summer days underneath dark-surfaced materials. Another natural source of heat is that generated by the bodies of mammals and birds. Reference again to Table 6 will show that warm-blooded animals appear to be involved in three different ways.

First, there are nesting materials, which have proved to be one of the only two sources thus far for *Myriococcum albomyces* and are particularly good sources for *Chaetomium thermophile* and *Torula thermophila*. The fungi presumably become established on the nesting materials, possibly with associated excreta, as a result of elevated temperatures (up to 35° or 40°C) during egg incubation or rearing of the young. But some doubt is cast upon this presumption by the frequency with which several of the thermophilic fungi have been found on ordinary straw (not derived from nests) and other plant substrata properly moistened and incubated (see Table 6).

Second, is the frequency with which the dung of herbivorous animals, from rabbits to elephants, has, when incubated, provided various thermophilic fungi—including, in fact, almost half of the forms listed in Table 6. Just what role, if any, the body heat of the animal plays in this case is not clear. It is most unlikely that the warmth of the dung, when deposited, would remain long enough to be of any significance. Nor is there any evidence of growth of the fungus in the animal's hindgut prior to defecation or of stimulation of spore germination from passage through the gut, as occurs in many coprophilic fungi. A much more likely explanation of the appearance of thermophilic fungi on incubated feces of herbivorous animals is the obviously likely presence of the spores of such fungi in the

hay or other fodder materials that these animals are generally fed. What-
ever the correct explanation, the dung of herbivores is a well-proved hunting
ground for thermophilic fungi.

Third, is the possibility—of special interest to Miehe (1907a), Noack
(1912), and many other investigators concerned with animal mycoses—
that thermophilic fungi might be favored by the body temperature of
homoiotherms and thus have become adapted to parasitic growth. This
has been clearly established, however, only in the case of the two species
of *Mucor*. When Lindt (1886) first described and named *M. pusillus*, he
was concerned about its pathogenic potentialities. Spore suspensions were
injected directly into the jugular vein of dogs, and death ensued within
a few days. Post mortem examinations revealed the fungus in various
tissues, and it was subsequently reisolated from such tissues. Lindt concluded that it was capable of pathogenesis. The species has been associated with animal mycoses on a number of occasions since then. Tscherniak
(1928) isolated it from a lung nodule in a horse; Baudet (1932) reported it
from a pig; Plum (1932) obtained it six times in isolations made from cows
that had aborted, and Jungherr (1935) too associated it with bovine mycotic abortion. Ainsworth and Austwick (1955) reported five isolations from
cattle, four from fowl, and one each from pig, dog, and duck. These workers also noted that the fungus was apparently involved in one case of
mastitis in cattle, but, like Plum (1932), they were unwilling to accept
pathogenicity as proven. In a subsequent publication Ainsworth and Austwick (1959, p. 50) stated that "*Mucor pusillus* is the only *Mucor* species
conclusively shown to be pathogenic." One of the Ainsworth and Austwick
(1955) isolates was found by Smith (1957) to be homothallic, and hence
we have included it in our new species *M. miehei* (see §3). Zycha (1935)
commented that the high temperature optimum of *M. pusillus* is certainly
correlated with its pathogenicity for dogs and other mammals.

Ainsworth and Austwick (1959, p. 53) list *Humicola lanuginosa* (their
Monotospora lanuginosa) as a cause of bovine mycotic abortion, reported
to them by de Vries in 1955 in a personal communication, but no further
details are given. This is a particularly interesting report since it represents
apparently the first record of *H. lanuginosa* as a parasite. In 1947 C. W.
Emmons (personal communication) informed us that, so far as he could
tell from preliminary animal inoculations, our own strains of *H. lanuginosa*
and *Malbranchea pulchella* var. *sulfurea* from guayule rets were nonpathogenic. Previous reports on *M. pulchella* (see §11) show that this
species has been found repeatedly to cause mycotic infections of man and

animals. None of the pathogenic isolates thus far has been thermophilic, however, so that none would be included in *M. pulchella* var. *sulfurea* as we are defining it. Nevertheless, it would seem well for medical mycologists to keep a watchful eye on all thermophilic species of fungi. Furthermore, it is not impossible that some of these species may be involved in one way or another in such little understood disturbances as "farmers lung" or the respiratory affliction suffered periodically by the workers in industrial mushroom beds. (See, for example, Fuller, 1958 and 1961; Dickie and Rankin, 1958; Bringhurst and Gershon-Cohen, 1959; Gregory and Bunce, 1961.) Quite understandably, no thermophile is mentioned in Togashi's (1949) book devoted entirely to the temperature relations of *plant* pathogens. There appear to be no vascular plants that can tolerate temperatures favoring the thermophilic molds.

In view of all the data presented in Table 6 and the special and probably fairly rare natural circumstances under which the growth of thermophilic fungi will occur, we are forced to conclude that viable spores of these microorganisms are probably very widespread, awaiting—as do the seeds of desert annuals—the right conditions for germination and growth. For the vast majority of spores, these conditions never materialize. But for those few that do encounter favorable conditions, growth becomes possible; an immense new supply of spores is rapidly produced and subsequently becomes spread far and wide in the dust and debris that remain following completion of the microbial action. Tsiklinskaya's (1899) original culture of *Humicola lanuginosa* was obtained simply by inoculating pieces of potato with garden soil and incubating at an elevated temperature. Hagem (1908) isolated *Mucor pusillus* from the air and Nielsen (1927) reported it from soil. Noack (1912) claimed that he could readily obtain thermophilic fungi from many natural substrates: soil, forest leaf mold, rotten wood, fruits, and animal hairs, besides birds' nests, excrement of all sorts, and other sources. Nevertheless, although the spores of thermophilic fungi are undoubtedly widespread, they are certainly most likely to occur on materials that have been through some natural process of microbial self-heating or have been held temporarily at temperatures around 35–55°C by some other agency. This general conclusion is borne out by the interesting data tabulated in Crisan's (1959, p. 29) thesis. These data clearly show that composted materials were a far more productive source of thermophilic fungi than were samples of muck soils, forest soil, or dung. Mishustin (1950, p. 299) also concluded that thermophilic fungi are poorly represented in the soil.

Other Possible Sources to be Explored

There are a number of other situations in which thermophiles might be expected to occur but where, thus far at least, no thermophilic fungi have been found. Both Miehe (1907a) and Noack (1912) considered that tropical regions of the world, with their milder climate and year-round high insolation, would be particularly favorable. A thorough search of such areas has not been made and might well be very rewarding.

Miehe (1907a) also discussed the possibilities afforded by volcanic regions and hot springs. He pointed out that such sites are often quite barren of organic material and hence could not be expected to support a large saprophytic microflora.* Hot springs are, of course, the classic locus of thermophilic algae and a variety of other organisms, and we are inclined to believe that fungi—very possibly aquatic Phycomycetes—will ultimately be found to occur there as well. Indeed, Molisch (1926), in his extensive reports on the biology of Japanese hot springs, noted the profuse occurrence of a septate mold at a temperature of 56.5°C at Yamagata-Ken. No further identification was made, and the material could conceivably have been moribund and colorless algal filaments. In our own work we made only one, tentative attempt to discover fungi in a hot spring. Water from Steamboat Springs, Washoe County, Nevada (about 10 miles south of Reno) was obtained and "baited" in the usual manner (compare Sparrow, 1960) with bits of cellophane, leaves, and onion skin. These cultures were incubated at 50°C for several days but no fungi appeared. However, further systematic and extensive studies along these lines must be carried out before any meaningful conclusions can be drawn.

One other unexplored and intriguing possible source of thermophilic microorganisms has come to our attention: the nests of a group of birds, the Megapodiidae or so-called incubator birds, which live in Australia and many of the islands of the Southwestern Pacific. Related to and about the size of domestic fowl, these extraordinary birds incubate their eggs in the warmth of large compost piles that they themselves prepare and tend with consummate skill. Recent accounts of their interesting activities and general biology are given by Frith (1959, 1962), who describes how they gather twigs and leaves and build them into a heap, how they measure the temperature of the pile by probing it with their bills, and how they work hours each day piling and unpiling the composting material to adjust for large

---

* But see Addenda, p. 158.

diurnal changes in temperature and insolation. So effective are their activities that the center of the mass, where the eggs are located, is held amazingly close to 92°F (32°C) for the entire five months or more during which eggs are being serially incubated and hatched out. Quite possibly some parts of these avian composts reach higher temperatures, and a detailed exploration of their microflora might be very rewarding. Sames (1900) made this suggestion more than sixty years ago, yet it still remains to be followed up.

16

HUMIFICATION AND COMPOSTING ACTION

The constant recurrence of thermophilic fungi on composting plant materials certainly suggests that they are actively involved in the decomposition processes that are taking place. However, relatively little information is available on the nature of their specific activities. Rege (1927), who appears to have been the first to undertake detailed studies of the role of thermophilic molds in the breakdown of cellulosic materials, stated that *Humicola lanuginosa* (his *Acremoniella* sp.) made little or no growth on a medium containing cellulose as the sole carbon source. He concluded, however, that high-temperature fungi probably play an important role in the decompositions occurring in self-heating manure. Stoller et al. (1937) used a slowly rotating drum to effect environmental control in larger-scale composts of horse manure and chopped cornstalks. Temperatures rose to 60°C or more, high levels of carbon dioxide were recorded, and dry-weight losses of 20–30 percent occurred. Isachenko and Mal'chevskaya (1936) and Mal'chevskaya (1939) claimed extensive cellulose breakdown in the central "semi-coke" regions of self-heating peat piles but presented little real evidence. *Talaromyces (Penicillium) duponti* (their *Citromyces sphagnicola*) was said to grow poorly on cellulose and attack it weakly, whereas *Thermoascus aurantiacus* (their *Thermoascus isatschenkoi*) did not attack cellulose at all. More detailed results on the composting action of thermophilic microorganisms were published by Waksman and his group in 1939. Waksman, Umbreit, and Cordon (1939) determined, for example, that a pure culture of their thermophilic fungus—evidently a species of *Humicola* (they called it *Thermomyces* but it probably was *Humicola insolens*, not *Humicola lanuginosa*; see below)—growing on stable manure for forty-two days at 50°C destroyed nearly 40 percent of the dry matter, doubled the water-soluble organic matter, and dropped the hemicelluloses from 22.8 to 17.2 percent and the celluloses from 19.7 to 12.6 percent. They concluded (1939, p. 47) that "The fungus was the only organism that approached the total population [i.e., the natural mixed thermophilic microflora] in the extent of decomposition. It decomposed 40 percent of the total manure, as compared with 62 percent for the mixed population. The fungus brought about the destruction of a greater than proportional amount of the hemicelluloses and cellulose, but it attacked the lignin only to a limited extent, as compared with the mixed population." Similar results were obtained by Waksman and Cordon (1939) in their investigation of the thermophilic decomposition of plant residues, such as 60 percent straw and 40 percent alfalfa, where their thermophilic fungus was again very active. They showed that the addition of calcium carbonate to the material favored compost formation by the fungus. In their third paper (Waksman, Cordon, and Hulpoi, 1939) they concluded that the temperature of the compost was one of the most important factors in controlling the rate of decomposition and the conservation of nitrogen. Thermophilic fungi and Actinomycetes were particularly active in the composts at 50°C.

Reese (1946) showed conclusively that *Humicola insolens* (his *H. grisea*) was an active cellulose decomposer but that *Humicola lanuginosa* (his *Monotospora lanuginosa*) could not attack cellulose. This finding of Reese—that *H. lanuginosa* is not a cellulose decomposer—agrees with Rege's (1927) and Norman's (1930) earlier but less conclusive observations. It also suggests that Waksman, Umbreit, and Cordon (1939) were working with *H. insolens* rather than with *H. lanuginosa* (Tsiklinskaya's 1899 *Thermomyces*) as they supposed. This bit of confusion is an excellent example of how important taxonomic work can be as an essential foundation for physiological observations. Kaila (1952), in her detailed studies of the humification of straw at various temperatures between 5° and 65°C, also isolated a thermophilic fungus, which she identified merely as "possibly some species of *Thermomyces*." Although she carried out pure-culture experiments at 50°C with this isolate, there is no way of knowing with certainty which species she was working with. She seemed surprised that her fungus effected little or no decomposition of cellulose whereas the thermophilic fungi of Waksman, Umbreit, and Cordon (1939) were active cellulose decomposers. Once again, the importance of positive identification is underscored. In her experiments Kaila used chopped or ground rye straw, supplemented with urea nitrogen and potassium phosphate. She came to the conclusion that, from a practical viewpoint, short-term decompositions at higher temperatures (50–65°C) could yield a valuable product in a short time. If she had had an active cellulose-decomposing thermophilic fungus, such as *Humicola insolens* appears to be, she might have been even more certain of the values of composting at temperatures around 50°C. At 65°C, of course, she found no mold activity at all because, as we know, there are no thermophilic fungi capable of vigorous growth above 60°C.

Contrary to Kaila, Henssen (1957b) described her isolates of the thermophilic fungi used in her studies of the decomposition of straw and stable manure so precisely that one can be confident of their identity. Moreover, we ourselves had the opportunity of examining her cultures of *Humicola*. She agrees with Rege (1927) and Reese (1946) in concluding that *Humicola lanuginosa* (her *Thermomyces lanuginosus*) will not decompose cellulose, but, like Reese, she demonstrated cellulose decomposition by *Humicola insolens* (her *Humicola* sp.). Moreover, she discovered a new thermophilic *Sporotrichum* and established that it decomposed cellulose weakly but vigorously attacked hemicelluloses and pectin. Using equal parts of rye, wheat, barley, and oat straw, supplemented with nitrogen and other nutrients, she carried out pure-culture experiments under carefully controlled conditions. Her general conclusions on composting and humification agree closely with those of Kaila (1952) and Waksman, Umbreit, and Cordon (1939). The thermophiles appear to be prominently involved in humification.

While it is clear, therefore, that at least two thermophilic fungi are concerned in cellulose decomposition at temperatures above 50°C, and all of the thermophilic fungi are active in the complex breakdown of plant materials at elevated temperatures, much remains to be learned about the precise nature of their activities. Further investigation of the breakdown of composting plant materials by identified cultures of thermophilic fungi would be most worthwhile.

17

ECONOMIC IMPORTANCE: THERMOGENESIS IN STORED AGRICULTURAL PRODUCTS

In the economy of nature at large, the thermophilic fungi have a certain importance in contributing, as we have just seen, to the general processes of breakdown of dead plant materials and the building of humus wherever the requisite temperatures are found. Furthermore, because they are involved in the preparation of farmyard manure and garden composts throughout the world, they have a value in agriculture that is of tremendous significance, though hard to estimate in any precise terms. They have also entered rather more directly into man's economy, probably since the earliest days of agricultural harvest and in a variety of fascinating ways. This economic aspect, while it is peripheral to the main purpose of our discourse, merits attention here and will be considered under two main headings: microbial thermogenesis by thermophiles in relation to spontaneous combustion and storage problems, and action or uses of thermophiles in industrial processes.

Most people have heard that damp hay may set a barn afire, but even today few will undertake to explain each step in the process in thoroughly logical and scientific fashion. Indeed, there has been a continuing controversy about the causes of spontaneous combustion of stored plant materials for a good many hundreds of years. Much heat has been generated by the argument itself, and only in fairly recent decades can it be said that essential agreement has been reached among the various schools of thought. An appreciation of the background of this interesting subject can be gained by reading Browne's (1929) account of the spontaneous combustion of hay.

There the reader will learn that Roman records reveal the good farmer's ancient respect for the dangers of damp hay and his attention to carefully spelled out procedures for proper curing and drying of agricultural products before storage. There he will find that Ferdinand Cohn (1889, 1891) first drew a distinction between the primary production of heat (thermogenesis) by the living cells of fresh plant material itself and secondary production of heat by saprophytic microorganisms growing on the dead and decaying plant material—that is to say, microbial thermogenesis. And there too he will become aware of the argument that persisted so long between those who maintained that the entire process was essentially chemical and had little or nothing to do with vital activities and others who held firmly to the belief that the heat generated by living cells played a critical part in the action. Among those who believed that microbial thermogenesis played a major role was Hugo Miehe, who devoted much of his life to intensive studies of the self-heating of hay. We have referred often to his comprehensive book (Miehe, 1907a), *Die Selbsterhitzung des Heus,* because it represents the first, and essentially the only detailed account of thermophilic fungi. However, Miehe was brought to a consideration of thermophilic microorganisms, not so much for their own sake, but rather because they provided an essential piece in his solution of the spontaneous combustion puzzle.

Cohn (1889) had shown that molding barley seedlings in an insulated container would heat to 60°C and that this heating, at least above 40°C, was probably due to the metabolic activity of the molds and could be curtailed or stopped by lack of air. He had also concluded (Cohn, 1891) that the heating to 57°C of packed, freshly cut grass was also due to microorganisms, as was the similar heating to 71°C of horse dung. Cohn's observations attracted much interest, but his conclusions were not generally accepted.

Soon after this, Miehe started a long and careful series of studies designed to elucidate the self-heating of hay and to clarify the role of microorganisms therein. Using a specially insulated chamber, he showed (Miehe, 1905, 1907a) that (1) damp, packed hay or leaves self-heated to 55° or 60°C within one to several days; (2) similar hay that was steamed, and hence probably largely but not entirely sterilized, did not heat; (3) steamed hay reinoculated with soil suspension or washings from untreated hay did heat; and (4) steamed hay inoculated with various pure cultures of microorganisms prevalent on self-heating hay, also heated. As a result of these experiments, Miehe became convinced that the heating of moist plant materials to 60° or 70°C was caused largely by microorganisms, and he set about making a thorough investigation of the microflora of self-heating hay and compost. We have already seen the rich harvest of thermophilic fungi he discovered, and his observations on thermophilic bacteria and Actinomycetes from this source are well known.

Following Miehe there was a long series of investigations over the next two or three decades, confirming and extending Miehe's conclusions and applying increasingly precise and controlled methods to the study of microbial thermogenesis. James (1927), for example, used Dewar flasks to provide the most effective insulation, and also supplied a slow stream of pure oxygen. With this same apparatus James et al. (1928) completely verified Miehe's results and showed that microbial self-heating also occurred in materials such as cornmeal, cracked corn, oats, and others. Furthermore, using pure culture inocula and cracked corn, which could be completely sterilized, they showed conclusively that (1) there was no heating whatsoever without inoculation, and (2) there was vigorous heating with appropriate individual microorganisms. *Aspergillus fumigatus*, for instance, raised the temperature of cracked corn to over 50°C. Norman (1930), in another thorough study, reached essentially identical conclusions.

Meanwhile, Miehe himself (1930a, 1930b) had provided much valuable additional information. He too was using Dewar flasks for better insulation, and he was achieving complete sterilization of his substrata. Having found that hay, when completely sterilized by autoclaving, was extensively altered chemically and unsatisfactory for growth of some of his microorganisms, he substituted bread as a nutrient and performed a series of precise experiments on the heating capacities of various pure cultures of both mesophilic and thermophilic organisms. He argued that if there were no thermophiles present in self-heating hay or other material, it should rise in temperature only to the point where the mesophiles were no longer able to thrive. For ordinary mesophilic fungi, this might be around 45°C, a level at which subsequent autocatalytic changes would take place, if at all, too slowly to initiate spontaneous combustion. If, however, thermophilic forms were present, they would take over at 40° or 45°C and their metabolism would now carry the heating to the higher levels (60–70°C) to which in fact it did rise. The fungi would be active up to 55° or 60°C and the bacteria and Actinomycetes would be involved at the highest temperatures, 60–70°C. Investigations of the microbial population (Miehe, 1907a; Webley, 1948a, 1948b; Niese, 1959; Glathe, 1960b) have shown that exactly this sort of change in the flora from predominant mesophiles to predominant thermophiles does, in fact, always occur. Moreover, by experiments in which he used pure cultures of individual fungi, Miehe (1930a) demonstrated

clearly that the temperature level reached with any given organism depended upon its own maximum for growth. Thus mesophiles such as *Rhizopus nigricans* or *Penicillium glaucum* could only raise the temperature to
35° or 40°C, whereas thermophiles like *Malbranchea pulchella* var. *sulfurea*
(his *Thermoidium sulfureum*) or *Humicola lanuginosa* (his *Thermomyces
lanuginosus*) raised the temperature to 60°C or above. These observations
have since been verified by Christensen and Gordon (1948) and numerous
other investigators. There can no longer be any question that the thermophilic microorganisms, and among them the fungi, are responsible for raising the temperature of self-heating plant materials to those levels at which
autocatalytic, essentially chemical processes can finally take over.

Thus the sequence of events leading to self-heating and ultimate spontaneous combustion of well-insulated hay and many other plant materials is
now generally agreed upon and has been repeatedly recorded in many
papers in more recent years (see, for example, Norman, Richards, and
Carlyle, 1941; Carlyle and Norman, 1941; Pallman et al., 1945; Hüni, 1954;
Niese, 1959; Glathe, 1960a). If the material is reasonably fresh, the initial
warming may be ascribed in part to the enzymatic activities of the still-
living plant material itself. However, it is generally conceded that the major
buildup of heat results from the metabolism of the mixed saprophytic,
microbial flora that promptly develops. The temperature rises quickly (see
Fig. 1), often in a matter of hours if the decomposing material is finely
divided and rich in readily available nutrient (such as fresh grass, chopped
guayule, or manure), and soon passes the optimum for mesophilic forms.
Here the thermophiles become of critical importance; they multiply rapidly
and raise the temperature to the peak that can be reached by microbial
activity—about 70°C or slightly higher. Subsequent heating results then
from the autocatalytic chemical processes which can begin to operate at
this temperature. These processes cause further heating, marked chemical
changes in the heating mass, and ultimate ignition if the necessary conditions are maintained. This final series of reactions, which lead to the actual
spontaneous combustion, is highly complex and, it seems, still not fully
understood. In any event the processes are clearly nonvital and require no
further consideration in this account of thermophilic fungi.

What is significant in evaluating the economic importance of thermophilic fungi is the realization that the thermogenesis and spontaneous combustion which they help to bring about cause very appreciable financial
losses in many parts of the world. Browne (1929) estimated losses of $20
million annually in the United States several decades ago, and more recently Glathe (1960a) indicated German losses of 2.5–7.9 million DM each

year. Both writers point out that these estimates are losses from fires; the damage and loss simply from overheating, without combustion, is not recorded and is probably very much larger in terms of reduced feed value. According to Glathe (1960a), there is only one good way to cut the losses from overheating or combustion, and this is to store hay and fodder at moistures of 20 percent or less. In another article (1960b) Glathe has also discussed the modern trend toward the use of microbiological evidence in legal cases where criminal incendiary action is suspected. If properly selected samples of hay can be obtained during or immediately after the fire, the thermophiles therein will indicate whether self-heating could have led to spontaneous combustion or not. Less than 0.01 percent thermophiles occur in normal hay that is not self-heated, whereas the ratio of thermophiles to mesophiles in self-heated hay will always be something over 1 percent, even though the heat of the fire has partially sterilized the sample taken. These tests are based upon counts of bacteria rather than fungi.

Hay and other types of fodder are not the only agricultural storage products that undergo microbial thermogenesis with possible subsequent spontaneous combustion. The self-heating and combustion of peat cause large economic losses also and have been extensively investigated by the Russians. Isachenko and Mal'chevskaya (1936) reported temperatures of 50°, 62°, and 75–80°C at depths of 10, 50, and 80 cm respectively in piled self-heating peat. They noted that fungi were particularly active and isolated several thermophilic species (see Table 6) besides Actinomycetes and bacteria. The self-heating of peat was also discussed by Mishustin (1950).

Plant products upon which man has depended for centuries and has stored in ever-increasing quantities are the various cereal grains and the flour and other food stuffs derived directly from them. Self-heating and even spontaneous combustion can also be a serious problem here (Gilman and Barron, 1930; Milner, Christensen, and Geddes, 1947; Christensen and Gordon, 1948). To our knowledge the only recorded instance of a truly thermophilic fungus being obtained from stored grain is Curzi's (1929) isolation of *Humicola lanuginosa* (his *Acremoniella thermophila*) from self-heated wheat in Italy. We have not undertaken an extensive review of the literature on grain storage, but papers such as those just cited indicate that molds are important in the heating of damp, stored cereals. With the present monograph on thermophilic fungi available for reference, it may be that future investigators of the microbiology of stored grain and flour will isolate and identify thermophilic fungi and demonstrate that they occur more commonly on such substrata than present evidence would suggest.

No doubt there are also numerous other agricultural products—cotton (see Cohn, 1893, for example), hemp, and such fibers, as well as hops and other plants—that undergo self-heating when they are moist and improperly stored. In all such instances where temperatures above 45° or 50°C are attained and mold growth is observed, investigators should be on the alert for the presence and activity of thermophilic fungi.

A few comments on the conditions affecting or controlling the heating process will serve to conclude this brief résumé of thermophilic fungi in microbial thermogenesis. As would be expected, moisture level, oxygen availability, and nutrient supply are of paramount importance. Each of the many investigators of microbiological heat production, beginning with Cohn (1889, 1891), has stressed one or more of these three factors. Representative papers will illustrate the sort of observations that have been made. James, Rettger, and Thom (1928) investigated thermogenesis in a number of plant materials. They found that vigorous heating up to 55° or 60°C occurred in hay at moistures between 40 and 60 percent. Pallman et al. (1945) reported temperatures of 60°C or more in fodder (hay) held at 26 to 40 percent moisture, and Hüni (1954) presented closely similar data; at 18 percent moisture, however, heating was only sufficient to reach 42°C. Glathe (1960a) and others have concluded that (as we noted just above) heating is insignificant at moistures below 20 percent. Isachenko and Mal'-chevskaya (1936) found most extensive heating in peat at 50 percent moisture, and there too prevention of undue heating and combustion can be achieved by proper drying. The cereal grains seem to require an even more reduced moisture to assure safe storage without heating. Wedberg and Rettger (1941) say that grains must be kept at 12 percent moisture or below, and Milner et al. (1947) place the level at 14.5 percent, at which point they found grain respiration only and no mold development. Grain storage is complicated by the warmth and moisture resulting from the respiration of the storage product itself and the tendency for the consequent development of damp pockets. Even diurnal temperature fluctuations in different parts of a grain bin can be sufficient to cause local deposition of moisture, molding, heating, and possible bin-burning. This whole question is vividly discussed by Christensen (1951) in his fascinating book on molds and man. Little or no molding occurs in cornmeal held at 13 percent moisture or below (Thom and LeFevre, 1921), and 16 percent moisture is about the critical level for stored flour (Barton-Wright and Tomkins, 1940).

The relation between oxygen supply and microbial thermogenesis is rather more difficult to investigate and, although many of the early workers like Cohn (1889, 1891) were aware that oxygen is essential for heating, few precise data are available. James (1927) seems to have been the first to relate levels of heating to known volumes of oxygen provided, and he and his co-workers (James, Rettger, and Thom, 1928) demonstrated wide temperature differences in various materials (cornmeal, cracked corn, wheat, hay, and so on) between the aerated samples and unaerated controls. Norman, Richards, and Carlyle (1941) also provided measured amounts of air to their cultures. Moreover, Norman (1930) and Carlyle and Norman (1941) showed a close correlation between evolution of carbon dioxide and microbial thermogenesis in both mixed and pure cultures. Glathe (1960a) stated that the heating of haystacks can be temporarily interrupted by the use of carbon dioxide, which interferes with aerobic respiration, but that this is not a useful way to control heating in actual practice.

Our own experience in the retting and heating of guayule (Allen and Emerson, 1949) has given us first-hand evidence of the essentiality of moisture between approximately 25 and 50 percent and of ready access to air. Whenever chopped guayule shrub was held at moistures below 20 percent or was packed in sealed drums at any moisture, heating was slight or undetectable. Evidently, for microbial metabolism to release enough calories from the substratum rapidly enough to cause pronounced self-heating, decomposing materials must be under aerobic conditions and at favorable moisture.

Another environmental factor affecting fungus thermogenesis was studied by Gaskill and Gilman (1939). They found, as would be expected, that addition of a utilizable nitrogen source markedly increased the degree of heating that occurred when individual fungi were grown on corncob meal in pure cultures under controlled conditions. Similarly, where other plant products such as straw are low in nitrogen (Carlyle and Norman, 1941), supplemental nitrogen will speed up metabolism and hence increase thermogenesis. Indeed, one can generalize from the few studies that have been done and conclude that all factors which tend to favor rapid and complete substrate decomposition will enhance microbial thermogenesis.

Finally, mention should be made of the relative thermogenic activities of different microorganisms in a mixed natural decomposition. In this account we have stressed investigations dealing particularly with fungi, but many observers have noted the extensive associated development of thermophilic bacteria and Actinomycetes. With their high rates of development and reproduction, it is not unlikely that these organisms are contributing very largely to the evolution of heat, although Miehe (1930a) credited molds with the larger share. At the present time there do not appear to be any precise data on this point, and such data might be rather difficult to obtain. For our purposes here it is sufficient to emphasize the facts that (1) fungi have been demonstrated to be actively thermogenic in pure culture; (2) various fungi are particularly well supplied with the enzymes necessary for decomposing complex plant materials; and (3) fungi are a very conspicuous component of the microflora of most self-heating, composting plant materials. The evidence seems overwhelming that thermophilic fungi play an important role in the aerobic decomposition and self-heating of composting plant materials.

18

ECONOMIC IMPORTANCE: ACTION IN INDUSTRIAL PROCESSES

Having considered the dangers of overheating and spontaneous combustion that result from the uncontrolled activities of thermogenic and thermophilic fungi as well as other microorganisms, we should recognize that these same organisms are used by man in a surprising array of manufacturing practices. Some of these go back into antiquity but others are relatively recent developments. Of particular interest are the so-called fermentations, in which the combination of microbial decomposition and heating produces the desired aroma or special flavor of the product. Both chocolate and tobacco come under this heading.

After the pulp and beans of cacao have been scooped from the pods, the material is gathered in mounds or "sweatboxes" and soon enters upon an active, natural decomposition (Chatt, 1953). Microbial thermogenesis is involved and the mass heats to 40° or 50°C for four or five days. Besides freeing the beans of the tenacious pulp and preventing them from germinating, the heat and the decomposition are an important part of the "cure" which imparts the desirable qualities to the chocolate. It appears that most of the favorable action in the fermentation of cacao is brought about by yeasts and bacteria, but two thermophilic molds have been obtained from decomposing cacao material (see Table 6). *Thermoascus aurantiacus* was isolated from pods in Holland, under circumstances that are not entirely clear. However, *Mucor pusillus* was derived (Lendner, 1929) from seeds and pulp that were fermenting and, by implication, heating.

Microbial fermentation is also an integral part of the processing of tobacco (Garner, 1946). In this case the previously dried—that is, "cured"—leaves are moistened and stacked in bales or large bins, to undergo a process called "sweating." The moisture ranges between 20 and 40 percent, adequate air is required, carbon dioxide is evolved, and the temperature reportedly rises to 50° or 60°C or more depending upon the type of tobacco being prepared. Various studies of this fermentation have been made (for example, Johnson, 1934; Reid et al., 1938), but, so far as we can determine, thermophilic fungi (as we define them) have not yet been obtained from self-heated tobacco. Evidently, when properly handled, sweating results mainly from the action of bacteria rather than molds. Nevertheless, Behrens (1892) long ago isolated *Aspergillus fumigatus* from the midribs of tobacco leaves that had heated to 57°C, so that "sweating" tobacco, as well as "curing" cacao beans, would seem to be a good place for further investigations of truly thermophilic fungi.

Mushroom growing provides a third example of the action of thermophilic microorganisms in industrial practice. Production of edible mushrooms is a thriving and often lucrative business in many parts of the world, and preparation of the beds for the spawn usually involves a typical microbial self-heating and composting of the carefully prepared mixtures of horse manure and straw or other ingredients. Atkins (1961) describes this as an aerobic process in which heating occurs to about 60°C for several days. The action (1) transforms the original material into an excellent substratum for the mushroom mycelium, and (2) destroys unwanted pests by performing a very effective sort of pasteurization. The decomposition of the readily available nutrients in the raw starting materials also prevents subsequent unwanted heating. From our own identification of cultures kindly provided by the Butler County Mushroom Farm in Pennsylvania, we know that several species of thermophilic fungi occur in mushroom composts, some of them very frequently (also see Addenda). Here again, however, we have little detailed knowledge of their specific activities. Doubtless they contribute to the heat that is generated, and doubtless too they are involved in the critical decomposition processes required for the production of a good mushroom bed. We noted earlier that Stoller et al. (1937) devised a rotating drum apparatus for controlled preparation of mushroom composts at high temperatures.

Mention may also be made here of another type of composting that is scarcely to be considered an industrial practice but may well become increasingly important in the future. The disposal of refuse and sewage in large cities has always presented a serious problem, and the odors that characterize the outskirts of many large cities attest to the fact that the problem has frequently been solved in a manner that is not only crude but also a health hazard. The possibility that such refuse, if properly treated, can provide valuable organic compost has long been recognized (Gotaas, 1956). Large-scale operations have been carried on successfully in Holland and various other parts of the world, but apparently few if any working schemes for regular disposal of refuse and garbage by composting have yet been established in the United States. The matter has been discussed in some detail by Golueke and Gotaas (1954), who reported development of a reliable procedure for composting municipal refuse, in which noxious insects and microbial pathogens were destroyed by the high temperatures (70–75°C) that resulted from microbial thermogenesis. Schulze (1962) also described a successful pilot-scale process in which garbage, sewage sludge, and waste paper were composted continuously in a rotating, aerated drum at temperatures ranging between 53° and 70°C. It is likely that economic considerations will prevent any immediate or extensive adoption of such processes, but it is noteworthy that, in their studies of inoculums for composts, Golueke, Card, and McGauhey (1954) reported two thermophilic fungi—*Talaromyces* (*Penicillium*) *duponti* and *Humicola* (*Thermomyces*) sp. If composting of garbage and refuse should ever become widespread, detailed knowledge of the activities of thermophilic fungi would be of practical importance.

Our own first acquaintance with thermophilic fungi was made during investigations of an industrial process relatively recent in origin and as yet hardly carried beyond the pilot stage in practice. Spence (1930, 1933) discovered that the quality of rubber obtained from guayule (*Parthenium argentatum*) can be markedly improved if the plant material is subjected to a process of decomposition, or retting, prior to milling. Allen et al. (1944) and Allen and Emerson (1949) established clearly that the critical feature of guayule retting is the microbial decomposition of resins; rubber from retted shrub has about 50 percent less resin contaminants and 50 percent greater tensile strength than the controls from unretted shrub. The true fungi were found to be a major and fundamentally important part of the flora in all of the stationary and even certain of the turned rets. Over forty species were isolated, representing about twenty genera of true fungi, and virtually every one of them was found to be capable, singly in pure culture, of bringing about the decompositions resulting in a good ret. Thus, it was concluded that nearly all the fungi found on retting guayule were active resin decomposers. Among these fungi, the thermophiles were, as we have observed, particularly involved at the temperatures of 40–60°C that developed in most of the successful, stationary rets. Table 7 summarizes the data on resin reduction effected by the thermophiles. Still more direct evidence of resin decomposition was obtained by growing the thermophilic fungi on resin-emulsion agar as described by Allen et al. (1944). Clearing of the emulsion by extracellular enzymes just in front of the advancing mycelium could be demonstrated in every instance. From these few data it will be apparent why our attention was first focused upon the true thermophilic fungi in our investigations of guayule retting. With the return to peacetime conditions and with advances in the technology of synthetic rubber, guayule has sunk back into obscurity, but the interesting observations on resin decomposition and thermophilism remain.

TABLE 7. Reduction of Resins in Guayule Rubber Resulting from Pure Culture Rets with Thermophilic Fungi.

Species	Period of Ret (Days)	Temperature of Ret (°C)	Resins in Crude Rubber		Change in Resins/Day (percent)	Clearing of Resin-emulsion
			Control	Retted		
Mucor pusillus	10	45	21.0	7.2	−6.6	+
Mucor miehei	7	37	18.7	8.6	−7.7	+
Talaromyces (Penicillium) duponti	7	45	18.1	10.8	−5.8	+
Thermoascus aurantiacus	7	37	18.7	10.3	−6.4	+
Humicola insolens	13	40	23.8	13.2	−3.4	+
Humicola lanuginosa	7	45	18.1	9.7	−6.6	+
Malbranchea pulchella var. sulfurea	7	45	18.1	9.6	−6.7	+

Another mycological development that attracted widespread attention during World War II was the production of penicillin. Stimulated, no doubt, by the idea that thermophilic organisms might exhibit unusually high growth rates and might therefore form metabolic products with particular rapidity, Rode, Foster, and Schuhardt (1947) made a search for antibiotics from thermophiles and reported that *Malbranchea pulchella* (probably our var. *sulfurea*) produced penicillin at 52°C. They found, however, a relatively low penicillin activity, which they ascribed, at least in part, to the rapid decomposition of penicillin at such a high temperature. Nevertheless these observations and the extensive earlier Russian work (Shaposhnikov and Manteifel, 1923) on production of citric acid by *Penicillium arenarium* (see §13) suggest that thermophilic fungi should not be overlooked in future explorations for organisms to use in microbial industry.

Last may be mentioned the peculiar process which the Germans have called "Futterverpilzung." After the emphasis we have placed upon agricultural losses from excessive microbial thermogenesis, it may be surprising to learn that self-heating and molding of fodders is currently being investigated as a means for actually improving the overall quality of fodder. According to recent papers by Müller (1961a and 1961b), the controlled thermogenic composting of fodder produces a feed that is better utilized and yields larger, healthier animals (pigs, chickens, sheep, and so on) than the controls fed on standard fodder. Some of the plant materials used were groats, bran, beets, and potatoes. They were prepared like compost, piled in shallow heaps, allowed to self-heat to 60°C, and used after 3 to 5 days. Müller has isolated many fungi from these composts, but, as we have noted in our account of temperature relations, he did not incubate his initial cultures at temperatures high enough to permit isolation of the thermophilic fungi that undoubtedly occurred and were active in these fodder composts. As research progresses on the bases for the improved effectiveness of such animal feeds, it will be increasingly important to isolate the members of the thermophilic microflora and interpret their role in the process of fodder preparation. It seems quite possible that their action is akin to the current practice of adding antibiotics to animal feeds.

19

PHYSIOLOGY

Although the first truly thermophilic fungus was described more than seventy-five years ago and our list now includes thirteen species, few fundamental studies have been made specifically on the physiology of these distinctive microorganisms. As will be apparent from the foregoing account of thermophilic fungi in composting and humification, a limited amount of fairly reliable information is now available on certain aspects of the nutrition and substrate utilization of certain species, notably *Humicola lanuginosa* and *H. insolens*. It is clear that *H. lanuginosa* is not a cellulose decomposer (Rege, 1927; Norman, 1930; Reese, 1946; Henssen, 1957b), whereas *H. insolens* is a vigorous cellulose decomposer (Reese, 1946; Henssen, 1957b). Reese (1946) studied in some detail the cultural factors that influenced the decomposition and even showed active cellulose breakdown by a cell-free extract prepared from his strain of *H. insolens*. Henssen (1957b) found that her thermophilic *Sporotrichum* could also use pure cellulose as a carbon and energy source, but growth under these conditions was less vigorous than when pectin or glucose was provided. Rege (1927) reported good or fair growth of *Humicola lanuginosa* on glucose, sucrose, maltose, mannose, galactose, xylose, starch, and lignin, and Reese (1946) also got good growth of *H. insolens* on glucose, maltose, xylose, and starch. Both investigators found that ammonium could serve as a nitrogen source for the *Humicola* sp. they were studying but that organic sources of nitrogen (such as asparagin, glutamic acid, or urea) were more readily available. We have seen no nutritional data for any of the ten other species of thermophilic fungi. However, the formation of resin-decomposing enzymes by *Mucor pusillus, M. miehei, Talaromyces (Penicillium) duponti, Thermoascus aurantiacus, Humicola insolens, H. lanuginosus,* and *Malbranchea pulchella* var. *sulfurea* was well established in our own work on guayule.

Noack (1912, 1920) is the only investigator who has devoted himself to specific, comparative physiological studies of thermophilic fungi. His first paper (1912) was concerned with the resistant capacities of the spores of

Mucor pusillus, Thermoascus aurantiacus, Chaetomium thermophile, Humicola lanuginosa, and *Malbranchea pulchella* var. *sulfurea.* He suggested that thermophiles, which find themselves only at rare intervals under the necessary elevated temperatures required for their growth, might be expected to have unusually well-developed capacities to withstand unfavorable conditions between times. Thus he studied particularly their resistance to low temperatures, to fluctuating temperatures, and to desiccation. In general he had to conclude that although the spores of thermophilic fungi can withstand ordinary temperatures occurring naturally in temperate regions of the earth and can remain viable for lengthy periods of desiccation, they do not appear to be any more adapted in this regard than are countless mesophilic species.

His later work (Noack, 1920) was concerned with metabolism, and most of his experiments were performed with *Thermoascus aurantiacus,* the most rapid grower of all the thermophiles. He measured carbon dioxide evolution during growth at optimum temperature and tabulated it as a percent of dry weight per twenty-four hours. Thus at 45°C *Thermoascus aurantiacus* produced 310 percent per twenty-four hours, *Mucor pusillus* 226 percent, and *Chaetomium thermophile* 117 percent. Hence rapidity of growth was directly correlated, as could be expected, with metabolic rate. However, even *T. aurantiacus* did not exhibit as high a rate of metabolism as one might expect at 45°C. Ordinary mesophiles, such as *Penicillium glaucum,* gave carbon dioxide at 67 percent of dry weight per twenty-four hours at 15°C and 133 percent at 25°C; extrapolation to 45°C gives over 500 percent, whereas *T. aurantiacus* showed only slightly over 300 percent. The Q_{10} for the thermophiles was also found to be somewhat lower than that for mesophiles. One gains the clear impression, therefore, from these pioneering studies, that the thermophilic fungi have not become adapted to high temperatures simply as a means to more rapid growth. The adaptation is a much more subtle one and involves obligate occupation of an ecological niche established by the temperature limits for growth. Noack (1920) must have recognized this interesting point because he turned his attention next to the all-important question of what happens to the metabolism of a thermophile at the lower end of its temperature range. He found that most of the mycelium of *T. aurantiacus* was killed by exposure to 20°C for a few days and all of it was dead after twenty-four days. He then demonstrated that carbon dioxide production dropped rapidly at subminimal temperatures, and the lower the temperature the more quickly the metabolism fell off. He concluded that the diminishing rate of metabolism was a result of progressive permanent damage to the protoplasm of the hyphae, and he could demonstrate the extent of this permanent damage by determining the respiratory rate at optimum temperatures before and after the cooling. The lower the temperature and the longer the exposure, the greater the permanent damage done. In no instance, however, was there any evidence of a change in the ratio of carbon dioxide to oxygen.

In contrast to its sensitivity to subminimal temperatures, *T. aurantiacus* was found (Noack, 1920) to be highly resistant to anaerobic conditions. Noack knew very well the likelihood of marked reduction in available oxygen in the inner regions of masses of decomposing plant material. He found that *T. aurantiacus* would continue to carry on metabolism, at a reduced rate but with no change in the ratio of carbon dioxide to oxygen, under conditions of marked oxygen lack and could withstand essentially anaerobic conditions for eight days. If the oxygen supply was returned to normal, following short periods of anaerobiosis, the respiratory quotient rose markedly for several hours. Extended periods of anaerobiosis ultimately caused death. It is interesting to note in this connection that Henssen (1957b) reported a capacity of *Humicola insolens* to grow under anaerobic conditions. Indeed, she stated that at the higher temperatures of its growth range this species grew better under anaerobic than under aerobic conditions. Detailed, quantitative studies on the metabolism of the thermophilic fungi are obviously urgently needed.

In closing this discussion of physiology, and as a fitting conclusion to our entire account of the thermophilic true fungi, we can raise once again the central question on the biology of thermophilic organisms: what is the basis of their thermophilism? This question has really two parts and there may well be two separate answers, for it is just as necessary to discover the basis for their failure to grow at ordinary temperatures as it is to understand their capacity to grow at elevated temperatures. We should recognize that mycologists have so far contributed no clues. For that matter, no definitive answers have yet been given, but it is the bacteriologists who are presently pointing the way, and anyone pondering these questions among the fungi should consider the relevant work on bacteria. A statement of the several hypotheses and reference to selected papers must serve to make the final point here.

Many years ago Setchell (1903), commenting upon the bacteria and blue-green algae that occur at such high temperatures in hot springs, noted that dehydrated proteins are more resistant to coagulation than are fully hydrated ones. But he said he had no reason to suppose that the water content of organisms found in hot springs was less than that of other related forms, and he decided that there must be some intrinsic difference between the proteins of mesophiles and those of thermophiles. Much of the recent work on thermophily in bacteria has been directed toward the very goal of discovering whether there are indeed demonstrable differences in the proteins of the two groups. After a lengthy study, however, comparing the enzyme systems of related mesophilic and thermophilic bacteria, Allen (1950, 1953) came to the conclusion that no basic differences between their proteins could be established. Metabolic processes were essentially similar, and there was no sharp dividing line between mesophiles and thermophiles. In fact, the property of thermophily could in certain instances be induced or removed simply by making a series of culture transfers at successively higher or lower temperatures. From these observations Allen was led to support an idea put forth earlier (compare Gaughran, 1947, p. 202) that, whereas the proteins of thermophiles are just as unstable at high temperatures as are those of mesophiles, thermophily depends upon a capacity for exceptionally rapid enzyme synthesis and steady replacement. This has become known as the "dynamic" hypothesis of thermophily.

Baker et al. (1953, 1955) found that thermophiles tend to show an increasing complexity of nutrient requirements with increasing temperatures, and they considered that this supported Allen's dynamic hypothesis because thermophiles at higher temperatures would require more ready-made building blocks to meet the requirement for rapid enzyme replacement. However, there is growing evidence to support another point of view— namely, that there exist, as Setchell suggested, proteins with special properties; this can be termed the "stable protein" hypothesis. Militzer and his colleagues (Militzer et al., 1949, 1951) have shown, for example, that certain widespread enzymes, such as malic dehydrogenase, in cell-free systems are heat-labile when obtained from mesophiles but heat-stable when obtained from thermophiles, even though apparently essentially identical in other respects. Somewhat contradictory results with other enzymes led them to suggest that in thermophiles some proteins might be innately stable whereas others could have stability conferred upon them by the presence of a special factor. Koffler and others (Koffler, 1957; Adye et al., 1957) have demonstrated that the nonenzymic proteins in bacterial flagella—so-called flagellins—are much more resistant to heat when derived from thermophiles than they are when derived from mesophiles. These investigators suggest that the greater stability of thermophile flagellins may result from a different degree of hydrogen bonding. Still more recently Manning and Campbell (1961) have obtained crystalline preparations of α-amylase from a thermophilic bacterium. The physicochemical properties of this protein are currently being intensively studied (Manning, Campbell, and Foster, 1961;

Campbell and Manning, 1961; Campbell and Cleveland, 1961) in an effort to discover the basis for its high heat-stability.

A third suggestion to account for thermophily is the so-called "converting principle" or "temperature factor" hypothesis. Sie, Sobotka, and Baker (1961) claim that thermophilic bacteria produce a dialyzable, heat-stable substance which, when extracted and incorporated in small amounts into growing cultures of mesophiles, will induce them to become thermophiles. A substance having similar properties appears also to be present in yeast autolysate, and efforts are being made to identify it.

Some of the most ingenious proposals have been made to explain the high minimum temperatures for thermophiles. What prevents them from growing at the ordinary temperatures at which their close relatives thrive? Swartz and his associates (1957) have discussed the evidence for a possible mechanism. If a particular enzyme that is fairly heat-stable is blocked by a specific protein inhibitor that is somewhat less heat-stable, activity of the enzyme will not take place until the temperature has risen high enough to destroy the inhibitor. Such systems have, in fact, been demonstrated in bacteria. The enzymes themselves, freed of their inhibitors, act like any other enzymes. That is to say, heat does not activate the enzyme molecule directly, it simply removes the inhibitor. Evidently enzyme-inhibitor complexes of this sort provide a possible basis for understanding the special minimum temperature characteristics of thermophilic fungi. Quite possibly the final explanation of both the high minimum and the high maximum temperatures that characterize thermophiles will involve all of the hypotheses and proposals just discussed and perhaps even others besides.

It is our hope that the present monograph will bring to the attention of mycologists, and general microbiologists as well, the variety of thermophilic fungi, their occurrence and activities in nature, and their biological characteristics. Then they may take their place alongside other thermophilic microorganisms in future efforts to define and interpret the basic biological phenomenon of thermophily.

Addenda

ADDENDA

During the time that our manuscript was being reviewed and prepared for the printer, several new reports of thermophilic fungi have been published and certain other matters have come to our attention. We regret that it is not possible at this juncture to incorporate the new material directly into the body of our text, but we feel that citations of the relevant literature and a brief review of the main points will be most helpful.

In his monograph of the Chaetomiaceae, Ames (1961) lists three species of *Chaetomium* as being thermophilic. These include *C. thermophile* La Touche, *C. britannicum* sp. nov., and *C. virginicum* sp. nov. From the descriptions of the two new species, it is evident that *C. britannicum* is sufficiently different from *C. thermophile* (the only previously described thermophilic species of *Chaetomium*) to warrant the rank of a separate thermophilic species. We are not convinced, however, that *C. virginicum*, which is very similar to the organism we have described as *C. thermophile* var. *coprophile*, is distinct enough from *C. thermophile* La Touche to be considered a separate species. Aside from some slight differences in the size of the perithecia and in the length of the asci, *C. virginicum* and *C. thermophile* are very much alike. The chief difference between the two organisms concerns the dichotomously branched perithecial hairs: in *C. virginicum* they completely cover the fruiting structure, whereas in *C. thermophile* the branched hairs are limited to the upper portion of the perithecium. The perithecia of our variety, *C. thermophile* var. *coprophile*, are also covered with branched hairs. We have stressed this character in considering our isolate a variety of *C. thermophile*, but we feel this one character alone is not sufficient evidence for considering either our variety or *C. virginicum* as a distinct species.

Ames does not indicate the temperature range within which his two new organisms will grow, but he simply states that relatively high temperatures (45–50°C, or higher) are necessary for the production of sexual fruiting bodies. We believe that until all thermophilic species of *Chaetomium* are compared, including a comparison of their temperature limits, no definite conclusion can be reached regarding the taxonomic disposition of these species.

Recently published or in press are valuable accounts of the thermophilic fungi from municipal refuse compost in Germany (Klopotek, 1962), from alluvial soils and plant debris in England (Apinis, 1963a and 1963b), from the dust from moldy hay in England (Gregory and Lacey, 1963), from paper mills in Canada (Eveleigh and Brewer, 1963), from mushroom composts in Switzerland (Fergus, 1964), and from peat in Ireland (Küster and Locci, 1964). A summary of these collections is presented in Table 8. They provide additional information about the distribution and activities of thermophiles. Of special significance, moreover, are the new species listed in Table 8. All but one (*Sporotrichum*) represent genera not hitherto included among the true thermophiles.

Allescheria terrestris Apinis is a particularly distinctive addition to the thermophilic fungi. It is a cleistothecial Ascomycete in the Eurotiales with a Cephalosporium conidial stage. The ascocarps are dark and small (100–200 μ) and have a membranous peridium. Asci are short-clavate and 14–20 × 6–8 μ. Ascospores are oval, smooth-walled, brown, and 4–6 × 3–4 μ. Apinis (1963a, pp. 69–71) noted similarities between his *Allescheria* and Noack's (1912) *Anixia* and concluded that Noack was mistaken in thinking he had *Anixia spadicea*. The implication is that Noack may have had a fungus like *Allescheria terrestris*. We have discussed the Anixia question in some detail, and in §7 we have suggested that Noack was probably dealing with a thermophilic *Chaetomium* similar to our *C. thermophile* var. *coprophile*. Thus, while we agree with Apinis that *Anixia spadicea* Fuckel should be removed from the list of known thermophiles, we believe that a comparison of the three organisms in question indicates that Noack's description fits our variety of *Chaetomium* more closely than it does *Allescheria terrestris* Apinis. Unfortunately no one (see Crisan, 1959; Apinis, 1963a) has yet succeeded in locating a specimen of Noack's fungus for study at first hand.

Three other points in the paper by Apinis (1953a) require comment. We have noted (§12) that Henssen (1957b) was the first to isolate a thermophilic *Sporotrichum*, but she did not give it a specific epithet, and hence *S. thermophile* Apinis is new. Also, Apinis renames *Humicola stellatus* Bunce as *Thermomyces stellatus* (Bunce) comb. nov., but we have presented (§9) the reasons for abandoning the name *Thermomyces*. Finally, we are not certain that the Apinis (1953a, p. 72) isolate designated Culture coll. no. 272 B.D.U.N. can be included under *Talaromyces* (*Penicillium*) *duponti*. It differs quite markedly in a number of important respects. The

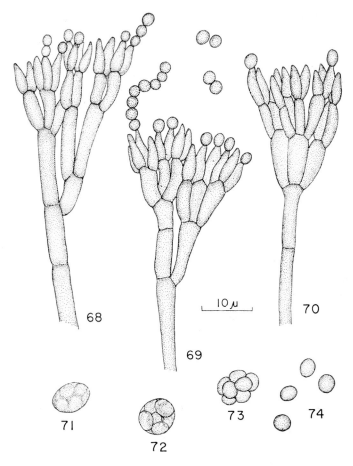

Figs. 68–74. *Byssochlamys* ? sp.
Figs. 68–70. Conidiophores, showing the various kinds of penicilli, and conidia borne in chains on the phialides. Figs. 71 and 72. Asci and developing asco-spores. Fig. 73. A cluster of 8 ascospores. Fig. 74. Free ascospores, revealing their smooth walls and lack of equatorial furrow or ridges.

conidia are larger and more irregular in shape, the ascocarps become brick-red at maturity instead of remaining nearly white, and, especially important, the ascospores are thin-walled and lacking any sort of equatorial furrow or ridges. Detailed comparisons will have to be made before we can be sure what the correct disposition of this interesting soil thermophile should be.

Another Penicillium-like thermophile has been causing some taxonomic difficulty. More than a year ago Blom and Emerson (1962) recorded their isolation from compost of a fungus believed by them to be a new *Peni-*

cillium. Its morphological features are illustrated in Figures 68–74. Its temperature range for growth is 30–60°C, and at 50°C (on a peptone-yeast-glucose agar) it forms a colony 9.5 cm in diameter in 4½ days, with a low, pale yellow surface mycelium and tan reverse. Phialides are 6–9 × 2.5–3.5 μ. Ascocarps are yellow, lacking any definite wall, and 0.2–0.8 mm in diameter. Ascospores are thin-walled, subglobose, smooth, yellow, lacking any equatorial furrow or ridges, and 3.2–4.1 × 3.0–3.4 μ. It was our initial thought that this organism could be classified as a *Penicillium,* possibly in the luteum group. However, Dr. K. B. Raper, Miss Dorothy I. Fennell, and Dra. A. C. Stolk (all in personal communications) have each expressed the opinion that our fungus is not a *Penicillium* and may more correctly be allied with species in the genus *Byssochlamys.* Since Dra. Stolk was already in possession of a very similar thermophile isolated from an Italian compost, she has undertaken to make a detailed diagnosis of both isolates and to provide a name for them in due course. It appears now that there may be quite a number of somewhat different thermophilic fungi in this Penicillium Paecilomyces-Byssochlamys complex and that they should all be made the subject of an intensive comparative investigation.

The thermophilic *Byssochlamys* sp. reported from slime in a Canadian paper mill by Eveleigh and Brewer (1963) is also in this complex, and the same may be true for the isolates of *Paecilomyces* made by Küster and Locci (1964) from peat. Dr. Küster has kindly given us an opportunity to examine these isolates. A good many of them grow very poorly at 50°C, but some do very well at this temperature and above and unquestionably fit our definition of true thermophily.

Another interesting addition to the growing ranks of true thermophiles is the *Stilbella thermophila* that Fergus (1964) obtained from mushroom compost. It is the first coremioid species in the group, and its possible association with some eurotialean perfect stage should be kept in mind. According to Fergus the hyphae are white to yellowish, the coremia are white and 280–360 μ high, the head is 48–130 μ in diameter and mucoid, and the conidia are borne singly on simple conidiophores and are colorless and average 22 × 9 μ.

We have not included in Table 8 Klopotek's (1962) *Hormiscium* sp. because the genus is generally considered to be synonymous with *Torula* (see Ainsworth, 1961), so that Klopotek's fungus is quite probably an isolate of *Torula thermophila.*

The quantitative data compiled by Klopotek (1962), Apinis (1963a, 1963b), and Gregory and Lacey (1963) are beginning to give us much needed information regarding such factors as seasonal distribution of ther-

TABLE 8. Recent Reports of Thermophilic Fungi from Specific Sources.

Species	Source	Authority[a]
KNOWN SPECIES		
Mucor pusillus	Refuse compost	Klopotek
	Soil or plant debris	Apinis
	Moldy hay	Gregory & Lacey
	Mushroom compost	Fergus
	Peat	Küster & Locci
Talaromyces (*Penicillium*) *duponti*	Refuse compost[b]	Klopotek
	Soil or plant debris (?)	Apinis
	Mushroom compost	Fergus
Thermoascus aurantiacus	Refuse compost	Klopotek
	Soil	Apinis
Chaetomium thermophile	Refuse compost	Klopotek
	Soil or plant debris	Apinis
	Mushroom compost	Fergus
Humicola insolens	Refuse compost (?)	Klopotek
	Mushroom compost	Fergus
	Peat	Küster & Locci
Humicola grisea var. *thermoidea*	Refuse compost (?)	Klopotek
	Mushroom compost	Fergus
Humicola stellata	Moldy hay	Gregory & Lacey
	Peat	Küster & Locci
Humicola lanuginosa	Refuse compost	Klopotek
	Soil	Apinis
	Moldy hay	Gregory & Lacey
	Mushroom compost	Fergus
	Peat	Küster & Locci
Malbranchea pulchella var. *sulfurea*	Refuse compost	Klopotek
	Soil or plant debris	Apinis
NEW SPECIES		
Allescheria terrestris n. sp.	Soil or plant debris	Apinis
Sporotrichum thermophile n. sp.	Soil or plant debris	Apinis
Stilbella thermophila n. sp.	Mushroom compost	Fergus
Byssochlamys (or *Penicillium*?)	Garden compost	Blom & Emerson
	Paper mill slime	Eveleigh & Brewer
Paecilomyces sp.	Peat	Küster & Locci

[a] See accompanying text for literature references.
[b] Specific identification of fungi from these sources was not clearly established.

mophiles and their prevalence in relation to stage and temperature of the decomposing substrate. Another important development is the demonstration by Loginova et al. (1962) that many obligately thermophilic microorganisms, including true fungi, occur in the thermal soils of volcanic regions in the Ural Mountains. No fungi were specifically identified in this first account, but it bears out Miehe's (1907a) contention that thermophiles would be found in volcanic areas.

Two new works on the physiology of high-temperature fungi merit emphasis. One, by Evreinova and Miroshnichenko (1962), is a study of the nucleotide ratios in mesophilic and thermophilic strains of *Aspergillus fumigatus;* the other, by Crisan (1962) is an account of his doctor's work on the nutrition, metabolism, and pigment production of *Humicola lanuginosa.*

Summary

SUMMARY

Thermophilism in the fungi, as defined in the foregoing study, relates to those fungi which grow only within the temperature range of 20° to 50°C or higher, with the maximum temperature, at which a known fungus (*Humicola lanuginosa*) will grow, occurring at 60°C. Forms such as *Aspergillus fumigatus, Absidia ramosa,* and others, which may grow at or near 50°C but which also grow well at temperatures below 20°C, are considered thermotolerant and are excluded from the true thermophilic fungi.

Thirteen species of thermophilic fungi were investigated, including four previously undescribed species and three new varieties of existing species. The fungi studied are listed here, with the minimum and maximum temperature required for growth given for each organism.

Mucor pusillus, 20–55°C
Mucor miehei sp. nov., 25–57°C
Talaromyces (Penicillium) duponti, 27–59°C
Thermoascus aurantiacus, 22–55°C
Chaetomium thermophile, 27–58°C
   C. thermophile var. *coprophile* var. nov., 27–58°C
   C. thermophile var. *dissitum* var. nov., 27–58°C
Myriococcum albomyces sp. nov., 26–57°C
Humicola grisea var. *thermoidea* var. nov., 24–56°C
Humicola insolens sp. nov., 23–55°C
Humicola lanuginosa, 30–60°C
Humicola stellata, 22–50°C
Torula thermophila sp. nov., 23–58°C
Malbranchea pulchella var. *sulfurea* comb. nov., 27–56°C
Sporotrichum thermophile, 24–50?°C

In addition to making extensive morphological investigations and reviewing the general taxonomy for each organism, specific contributions of the present study include: (1) The demonstration of the heterothallic nature of *Mucor pusillus* Lindt, based on matings between several strains of this species, and the separation and naming of *M. miehei,* a similar homothallic organism, as a distinct and new species. (2) The proposal to consider the genus *Myriococcum* as a bona fide member of the Ascomycetes, in the order Pseudosphaeriales, because of our proof of the presence of asci and ascospores in our new heterothallic species *Myriococcum albomyces*. (3) The suggested removal of *Anixia spadicea* Fuckel from the list of known thermophiles because of the discrepancies existing between different descriptions of *A. spadicea* and because the type culture, whose thermophilic nature has never been clearly established, apparently no longer exists. (4) The proposal to remove the genus *Malbranchea* from the Actinomycetes and place the genus in the Eumycota. This change is based on the relatively broad hyphae, the large spores, and the presence of discrete nuclei in the fertile hyphae of members of this genus.

There is no real evidence that thermophilic fungi tend to occur more commonly in one class of fungi than in another, for the Phycomycetes, Ascomycetes, and Fungi Imperfecti all are represented by thermophilic forms. Only the Basidiomycetes appear to be an exception to this, for at the present time only a few species of *Coprinus* appear to be able to grow at elevated temperatures. However, since these also grow well below 20°C, they cannot be considered as true thermophiles.

Most of the thermophilic fungi have been isolated from different types of composting plant materials such as guayule, straw, hay, grass, leaf mold, mushroom compost, and peat, and from different animal excrement including that of the horse, cow, sheep, goat, rabbit, pig, and elephant. A few have been found to occur in nesting material of fowl, specifically in straw from chicken nests, and from *Typha* straw from the nest of the coot. Occasional isolations have been made from stored grains and from other miscellaneous materials. Three species have been reported as causing animal mycoses. *Mucor pusillus* has been isolated from such animals as the dog, cow, pig, fowl, and horse, while *Mucor miehei* has been associated with a mycotic infection in the brain of a calf, and *Humicola lanuginosa* has been reported as the cause of mycotic abortion in cattle. Although soils thus far have proved to be a poor source of thermophiles, a more intensive search, particularly in regions with continuous or intense insolation such as the tropics, may reveal the presence of new thermophilic forms. Further investigation should also be made of hot springs, for so far as can be determined, no thermophilic aquatic fungi have ever been isolated.

It has been clearly demonstrated that thermophilic fungi play an important role in the decomposition of certain plant materials. Certain of these organisms have been definitely associated with the process of microbial thermogenesis and the subsequent breakdown of such material as manure, hay, guayule, mushroom compost, and other composting material. Undoubtedly, they also play a part in instances of spontaneous combustion of stored hay and grain.

Except for the few investigations dealing with nutrition and substrate utilization, little work has been done in connection with the physiology of these fungi. Even the basic question concerning the mechanisms of thermophilism in this group remains unanswered. This question—and others concerning these fungi—is in need of intensive investigation.

Finally, it is evident from our own investigations, as well as those of others, that the successful enrichment and isolation of thermophilic fungi from mixed, natural microbial floras depends largely upon the incubation of initial cultures at temperatures no lower than 45° or 50°C. At these temperatures the thermophiles are sufficiently favored to outgrow most mesophilic or thermotolerant forms. All of our laboratory studies were based upon detailed examination of pure cultures of each of the species reported here.

References

References

ADYE, JIMMY, HENRY KOFFLER, and G. E. MALLETT
  1957. The relative thermostability of flagella from thermophilic bacteria. *Arch. Biochem. Biophys.*, **67**:251–253.

AINSWORTH, G. C.
  1961. *Ainsworth and Bisby's Dictionary of the Fungi* (5th ed.). viii & 547 pp. Commonwealth Mycological Institute, Kew.

AINSWORTH, G. C., and P. K. C. AUSTWICK
  1955. A survey of animal mycoses in Britain: mycological aspects. *Trans. Brit. Mycol. Soc.*, **38**:369–386.

AINSWORTH, G. C., and P. K. C. AUSTWICK
  1959. *Fungal Diseases of Animals.* xi & 148 pp. Commonwealth Agricultural Bureaux, Farnham Royal.

ALEXOPOULOS, C. J.
  1952. *Introductory Mycology.* xiii & 482 pp. Wiley, New York.

ALLEN, MARY B.
  1950. The dynamic nature of thermophily. *J. Gen. Physiol.*, **33**:205–214.

ALLEN, MARY B.
  1953. The thermophilic aerobic sporeforming bacteria. *Bacteriol., Rev.*, **17**: 125–173.

ALLEN, P. J., and RALPH EMERSON
  1949. Guayule rubber, microbiological improvement by shrub retting. *Ind. Eng. Chem.*, **41**:346–365.

ALLEN, P. J., J. NAGHSKI, and S. R. HOOVER
  1944. Decomposition of guayule resins by microorganisms. *J. Bacteriol.*, **47**: 559–570.

AMES, L. M.
  1961. A monograph of the Chaetomiaceae. *U.S. Army Res. Devel. Ser.*, No. 2, ix & 125 pp.

APINIS, A. E.
  1963a. Occurrence of thermophilous microfungi in certain alluvial soils near Nottingham. *Nova Hedwigia, Zeitschr. Kryptogamenk.*, **5**:57–78.

APINIS, A. E.
  1963b. Thermophilous fungi of coastal grasslands. Pp. 427–438 in *Soil Organisms, Proceedings of the Colloquium on Soil Fauna, Soil Microflora and*

their Relationships by J. Doeksen and J. van der Drift (eds.). North-Holland, Amsterdam.

ARIMA, K., et al.
 1957.   Yeasts. 246 pp. Academic Press, New York.

ATKINS, F. C.
 1961.   *Mushroom Growing To-day* (4th ed.), 186 pp. Faber and Faber, London.

BAKER, HERMAN, S. H. HUTNER, and H. SOBOTKA
 1955.   Nutritional factors in thermophily: a comparative study of bacilli and Euglena. *Ann. New York Acad. Sci.*, **62**:349–376.

BAKER, HERMAN, H. SOBOTKA, and S. H. HUTNER
 1953.   Growth requirements of some thermophilic and mesophilic bacilli. *J. Gen. Microbiol.*, **9**:485–493.

BALDACCI, E., R. CIFERRI, and E. VACCARI
 1939.   Revisione sistematica del genere Malbranchea Sacc. *Atti Ist. Bot. "Giovanni Briosi" e Lab. Crittog. Ital. Univ. Pavia Ser. 4*, **11**:75–103.

BARTON-WRIGHT, E. C., and R. G. TOMKINS
 1940.   The moisture content and growth of mould in flour, bran, and middlings. *Cereal Chem.*, **17**:332–342.

BAUDET, E. A. R. F.
 1932.   Mucor pusillus Lindt als oorzaak van mycose bij het varken. *Tidschr. voor Diergeneesk.*, **59**:1163–1164.

BEHRENS, J.
 1892.   Ueber ein bemerkenswerthes Vorkommen und die Perithecien des Aspergillus fumigatus. *Centralbl. Bakteriol. Parasitenk.*, **11**:335–337. (This series subsequently became designated as *Zentralbl. Bakteriol. Parasitenk. Infektionskr. Hyg. Abt 1 Orig.*)

BENJAMIN, C. R.
 1955.   Ascocarps of Aspergillus and Penicillium. *Mycologia*, **47**:669–687.

BIOURGE, P.
 1923.   Les moisissiures du groupe Penicillium Link. *La Cellule*, **33**:5–331.

BISBY, G. R.
 1953.   *An Introduction to the Taxonomy and Nomenclature of Fungi* (2nd ed.). vii & 143 pp. Commonwealth Mycological Institute, Kew.

BLAKESLEE, A. F.
 1904.   Sexual reproduction in the Mucorineae. *Proc. Amer. Acad. Arts Sci.*, **40**:205–319.

BLOM, B. D., and RALPH EMERSON
 1962.   Studies on thermophily in fungi with particular reference to a new thermophilic Penicillium. *Amer. J. Bot.*, **49**:665. (Abstract of paper presented at the annual meeting of the Botanical Society of America.)

BOLOGNESI, G., and G. A. CHIURCO
   1925. Sopra una nuova micosi del torace ("Malbranchea Bolognesi-Chiurco"-Vuillemin, Pollacci et Nannizzi). *Arch Biol. (Genoa) Nuova Ser.*, 1: 255–276. (Even though the only date on the cover of this issue is 1924, dates given in the body of the paper show that it must have been published in 1925.)

BRINGHURST, L. S., and JACOB GERSHON-COHEN
   1959. Respiratory disease of mushroom workers, farmer's lung. *J. Amer. Med. Assoc.*, 171:15–18.

BROWN, AGNES H. S., and GEORGE SMITH
   1957. The genus Paecilomyces Bainier and its perfect stage Byssochlamys Westling. *Trans. Brit. Mycol. Soc.*, 40:17–89.

BROWNE, C. A.
   1929. The spontaneous combustion of hay. U.S. Dept. of Agric. Tech. Bull. No. 141, pp. 1–38.

BRUES, C. T.
   1927. Animal life in hot springs. *Quart. Rev. Biol.*, 2:181–203.

BUNCE, MAUREEN E.
   1961. Humicola stellatus sp. nov., a thermophilic mould from hay. *Trans. Brit. Mycol. Soc.*, 44:372–376.

CAMPBELL, L. L., and P. D. CLEVELAND
   1961. Thermostable α-amylase of Bacillus stearothermophilus. IV. Amino-terminal and carboxyl-terminal amino acid analysis. *J. Biol. Chem.*, 236:2966–2969.

CAMPBELL, L. L., and G. B. MANNING
   1961. Thermostable α-amylase of Bacillus stearothermophilus. III. Amino acid composition. *J. Biol. Chem.*, 236:2962–2965.

CANTINO, E. C.
   1956. The relation between cellular metabolism and morphogenesis in Blasto-cladiella. *Mycologia*, 48:225–240.

CARLYLE, R. E., and A. G. NORMAN
   1941. Microbial thermogenesis in the decomposition of plant materials. Part II. Factors involved. *J. Bacteriol.*, 41:699–724.

CARMICHAEL, J. W.
   1957. Geotrichum candidum. *Mycologia*, 49:820–830.

CAVARA, VITTORIANO
   1913. Una forma nuova di cheratomicosi (cheratomicosi mucorina). *Ann. Ottalmol.*, 42:650–674.

CHATT, EILEEN M.
   1953. *Cocoa: Cultivation, Processing, Analysis.* xvi & 302 pp. Interscience, New York.

CHIVERS, A. H.
  1915. A monograph of the genera Chaetomium and Ascotricha. *Mem. Tor.
          Bot. Club,* **14**:155–240.

CHRISTENSEN, C. M.
  1946. The quantitative determination of molds in flour. *Cereal Chem.,* **23**:
          322–329.

CHRISTENSEN, C. M.
  1951. *The Molds and Man.* viii & 244 pp. University of Minnesota Press,
          Minneapolis.

CHRISTENSEN, C. M., and DOROTHY R. GORDON
  1948. The mold flora of stored wheat and corn and its relation to heating of
          moist grain. *Cereal Chem.,* **25**:40–51.

CLEMENTS, F. E., and C. L. SHEAR
  1931. *The Genera of Fungi* vii & 496 pp. Wilson, New York.

COCHRANE, V. W.
  1958. *Physiology of Fungi.* xiii & 524 pp. Wiley, New York.

COHN, FERDINAND
  1889. Über thermogene Wirkung von Pilzen. *Jahresber. Schles. Geselsch.
          vaterl. Kult.,* **66**:150–156.

COHN, FERDINAND
  1891. Ueber Wärme-Erzeugung durch Schimmelpilze und Bakterien. *Jahres-
          ber. Schles. Geselsch. vaterl. Kult.,* **68**:23–29.

COHN, FERDINAND
  1893. Ueber thermogene Bacterien. *Ber. deutsch. bot. Geselsch., Bericht
          über die Verhandlung der zehnten General-Versammlung,* **11**:66–69.

COOK, A. H.
  1958. *The Chemistry and Biology of Yeasts.* xii & 763 pp. Academic Press,
          New York.

COONEY, D. G.
  1952. Morphology and taxonomy of the thermophilic fungi. Unpublished
          Ph.D. thesis, University of California, Berkeley. v & 111 pp.

COPELAND, J. J.
  1936. *Yellowstone Thermal Myxophyceae.* vi & 229 pp. Ann. New York Acad.
          Sci., Vol. 36.

CORDA, A. C. J.
  1837. *Icones fungorum hucusque cognitorum.* Tom. 1, 32 pp. J. G. Calve,
          Prague.

CORDA, A. C. J.
  1842. *Icones fungorum hucusque cognitorum.* Tom. 5, 92 pp. F. Ehrlich,
          Prague.

CRISAN, E. V.
  1959. The isolation and identification of thermophilic fungi. Unpublished
          M.S. thesis, Purdue University, Lafayette, Ind. 107 pp.

CRISAN, E. V.
1962. Growth and pigmentation of Monotospora lanuginosa (Tsil.) Mason. Unpublished Ph.D. thesis, Purdue University, Lafayette, Ind. 56 pp.

CURZI, MARIO
1929. Su una "Pseudocarie" delle cariossidi di frumento. *Atti Ist. Bot. "Giovanni Briosi" e Lab. Crittog. Ital. Univ. Pavia Ser.* 4, **1**:151–155.

CURZI, MARIO
1930. Ricerche morfologiche e sperimentali su un micromicete termofilo (Acremoniella thermophila Curzi). *Boll. R. Staz. Pat. Veg.*, Rome, N.S. Anno **10**: 222–280.

DICKIE, HELEN A., and JOHN RANKIN
1958. Farmer's lung, an acute granulomatous interstitial pneumonitis occurring in agricultural workers. *J. Amer. Med. Assoc.*, **167**:1069–1076.

DODGE, C. W.
1935. *Medical Mycology.* 900 pp. Mosby, St. Louis.

ELISEI, F. G.
1940. Nuova reperto e nuova interpretazione morfologica e sistematica di Malbranchea pulchella Sacc. et Penz., considerata come una nuova specie e un nuovo genere di dermatofiti. *Atti Ist. Bot. "Giovanni Briosi" e Lab. Crittog. Ital. Univ. Pavia Ser.* 4, **12**:141–200.

ELLIS, J. B., and B. M. EVERHART
1891. New North American fungi. *Proc. Acad. Nat. Sci. Philadelphia 1890* [**42**]:219–249.

ELLIS, J. B., and B. M. EVERHART
1892. *The North American Pyrenomycetes.* iii & 793 pp. Ellis and Everhart, Newfield, N.J.

EMERSON, RALPH
1941. An experimental study of the life cycles and taxonomy of Allomyces. *Lloydia*, **4**:77–144.

EMERSON, RALPH, and E. C. CANTINO
1948. The isolation, growth, and metabolism of Blastocladia in pure culture. *Amer. J. Bot.*, **35**:157–171.

EMMONS, C. W., and B. O. DODGE
1931. The ascocarpic stage of species of Scopulariopsis. *Mycologia*, **23**:313–331.

ENGLER, A., and K. PRANTL
1897. Die natürlichen Pflanzenfamilien. Teil 1, Abt. 1. viii & 513 pp. W. Engelmann, Leipzig.

EULER, HANS VON, and INGVAR LAURIN
1920. Zur Kenntniss der Hefe Saccharomyces Thermantitonum. II. Mitteilung. *Biochem. Zeitschr.*, **102**:258–267.

EVELEIGH, D. E., and D. BREWER
1963. Studies on slime accumulation in pulp and paper mills VI. Isolation of

thermophilic and thermotolerant fungi from paper mills. *Canad. J. Bot.*, **41**:1377–1382.

EVREINOVA, T. N., and G. P. MIROSHNICHENKO
  1962. Free nucleotides of the thermophilic and mesophilic variants of Aspergillus fumigatus. *Mikrobiologiya*, **31**:428–433. (In Russian with English
  summary. A full translation into English appears in *Microbiology*, **31**:
  350–354.)

FERGUS, C. L.
  1964. The thermophilic and thermotolerant molds and Actinomycetes of mushroom compost during peak heating. *Mycologia*, **56**:267–284.

FRIES, ELIAS
  1823. *Systema mycologicum.* Vol. 2. pp. 1–621. Berling, Lund.

FRIES, ELIAS
  1832. *Systema mycologicum.* Vol. 3. Part 2. pp. 260–524. Ernest Maurice,
  Greifswald.

FRITH, H. J.
  1959. Incubator birds. *Sci Amer.*, **201**:52–58.

FRITH, H. J.
  1962. *The Mallee-fowl, the Bird that Builds an Incubator.* xii & 136 pp. Angus
  and Robertson, Sydney.

FUCKEL, LEOPOLD
  1870. Symbolae mycologicae. Beiträge zur Kenntniss der Rheinischen Pilze.
  Jahrb. Nassauischen Ver. Naturk., **23** and **24**:1–459.

FULLER, C. J.
  1958. Farmer's lung. pp. 138–141 *in* Riddel, R. W., and G. T. Stewart (eds.),
  Fungous Diseases and Their Treatment. xvii & 256 pp. Butterworth,
  London.

FULLER, C. J.
  1961. Farmer's lung. *Internat. Arch. Allergy Appl. Immunol.*, **19**:314–315.
  (Abstract of paper presented to the British Association of Allergists.)

GARNER, W. W.
  1946. *The Production of Tobacco.* xiii & 516 pp. Blakiston, Philadelphia.

GASKILL, J. O., and J. C. GILMAN
  1939. Role of nitrogen in fungous thermogenesis. *Plant Physiol.*, **14**:31–53.

GAUGHRAN, E. R. L.
  1947. The thermophilic microorganisms. *Bacteriol. Rev.*, **11**:189–225.

GILMAN, J. C., and D. H. BARRON
  1930. Effect of molds on temperature of stored grain. *Plant Physiol.*, **5**:565–
  573.

GLATHE, HANS
  1960a. Selbsterhitzung und Selbstenzündung von Erntestoffen und ihre Ver-
  hütung. *Ergeb. landwirtsch. Forsch.*, **3**:83–98.

GLATHE, HANS
  1960b. Die mikrobiologische Analyse im Dienste der Brandursachenermitt-
        lung. *Kriminalistik: Zeitschr. gesam. kriminal. Wissensch. Praxis*, **14**:
        121–123.

GOLUEKE, C. G., B. J. CARD, and P. H. McGAUHEY
  1954. A critical evaluation of inoculums in composting. *Appl. Microbiol.*, **2**:
        45–53.

GOLUEKE, C. G., and H. B. GOTAAS
  1954. Public health aspects of waste disposal by composting. *Amer. J. Public
        Health*, **44**:339–348.

GOTAAS, H. B.
  1956. *Composting, Sanitary Disposal and Reclamation of Organic Wastes.*
        World Health Organization Monograph Series No. 31. 205 pp. World
        Health Organization, Geneva.

GREATHOUSE, G. A., and L. M. AMES
  1945. Fabric deterioration by thirteen described and three new species of
        Chaetomium. *Mycologia*, **37**:138–155.

GREGORY, P. H., and MAUREEN E. BUNCE
  1961. The microflora of hay. *Internat. Arch. Allergy Appl. Immunol.*, **19**:314.
        (Abstract of paper presented to the British Association of Allergists.)

GREGORY, P. H., and MAUREEN E. LACEY
  1963. Mycological examination of dust from mouldy hay associated with
        Farmer's Lung disease. *J. Gen. Microbiol.*, **30**:75–88.

GRIFFON, E., and A. MAUBLANC
  1911. Deux moisissures thermophiles. *Bull. Soc. Mycol. France*, **27**:68–74.

HAGEM, OSCAR
  1908. Untersuchungen über Norwegische Mucorineen. *Videnskabs-Selskabets
        i Christiania, Skrifter, 1 Math.-Naturv. Kl.* 1907, No. 7, pp. 1–50. (Now
        Norske Videnskaps-akademi, Oslo.)

HANSEN, H. N.
  1938. The dual phenomenon in imperfect fungi. *Mycologia*, **30**:442–455.

HANSEN, H. N., and W. C. SNYDER
  1943. The dual phenomenon and sex in Hypomyces solani f. cucurbitae.
        Amer. J. Bot., **30**:419–422.

HARKNESS, H. W.
  1884. New species of Californian fungi. *Bull. Calif. Acad. Sci.*, **1**:29–47.

HAWKER, LILIAN E.
  1950. *Physiology of Fungi.* xvi & 360 pp. University of London Press, London.

HENSSEN, AINO
  1957a. Beiträge zur Morphologie und Systematik der thermophilen Actinomy-
        ceten. *Arch. Mikrobiol.*, **26**:373–414.

HENSSEN, AINO
  1957b. Über die Bedeutung der thermophilen Mikroorganismen für die Zer-
         setzung des Stallmistes. *Arch. Mikrobiol.*, **27**:63–81.

HESSELTINE, C. W.
  1955. Genera of Mucorales with notes on their synonymy. *Mycologia*, **47**:344–
         363.

HOFFMANN, HERMANN
  1863. *Icones analyticae fungorum. Abbildungen und Beschreibungen von
         Pilzen mit besonderer Rücksicht auf Anatomie und Entwickelungsge-
         schichte.* 105 pp. J. Ricker, Giessen. (Heft I, 1861, pp. 1–32; Heft II,
         1862, pp. 33–56; Heft III, 1863, pp. 57–78; Heft IV, 1865, pp. 79–
         105.)

HUGHES, S. J.
  1953. Conidiophores, conidia, and classification. *Canad. J. Bot.*, **31**:577–659.

HÜNI, K.
  1954. Die Selbstentzündung von Heu. Pp. 264–279 in *Brandermittlung;
         Bericht über die 7. kriminalistische Arbeitstagung des Polizei-Instituts
         Hiltrup, bei der Bayerischen Versicherungskammer in München unter
         Mitwirkung des Bayerischen Landeskriminalamtes vom 3. bis. 6. No-
         vember 1953.* [Bavaria] Versicherungskammer, Abt. für Brandver-
         sicherung, Munich.

INGRAHAM, J. L.
  1962. Temperature relationships. Pp. 265–296. in *The Bacteria* by I. C. Gun-
         salus and R. Y. Stanier (eds.), Vol. IV. Academic Press, New York.

ISACHENKO (ISAČENKO), B. L., and N. N. MAL'CHEVSKAYA (MALČEVSKAJA)
  1936. Biogenic spontaneous heating of peat. *Dokl. Akad. Nauk SSSR*, **13**:377–
         380. (In English, with German summary.)

JAMES, L. H.
  1927. Studies in microbial thermogenesis I. Apparatus. *Science*, **65**:504–506.

JAMES, L. H., L. F. RETTGER, and C. THOM
  1928. Microbial thermogenesis II. Heat production in moist organic materials
         with special reference to the part played by microorganisms. *J. Bac-
         teriol.*, **15**:117–141.

JOHNSON, GROVE
  1905. Saccharomyces thermantitonum. *J. Inst. Brew.*, **11**:466–490. (A de-
         tailed account of this same work subsequently appeared in April, 1906,
         in German in the *Wochenschrift für Brauerei*, vol. 23, pp. 200–202,
         but this is merely a second-hand report, not an original paper.)

JOHNSON, JAMES
  1934. Studies on the fermentation of tobacco. *J. Agric. Res.*, **49**:137–160.

JOURDE, ANTOINE
  1908. Étude de quelques moisissures thermophiles. Ph.D. thesis, University
         of Paris. 113 pp. Lons-Le-Saunier, Paris.

JUNGHERR, ERWIN
    1935.   Mycotic affections of the bovine reproductive system. *J. Amer. Vet. Med. Assoc.*, **86**:64–75.

KAILA, ARMI
    1952.   Humification of straw at various temperatures. *Suom. Maataloust. Seur. Julk.* (*Acta Agr. Fenn.*), **78.3**:1–32.

KAMBAYASHI, T.
    1934.   Über ein von einer Spezies der Malbranchea hervorgerufenes Hautleiden in China. *Arch. Dermatol. Syph.*, **170**:97–106.

KANOUSE, BESSIE B.
    1923.   The life-history of a new homothallic Mucor. *Pap. Mich. Acad. Sci., Arts, Let.*, **3**:123–130.

KLOPOTEK, AGNES VON
    1962.   Über das Vorkommen und Verhalten von Schimmelpilzen bei der Kompostierung städtischer Abfallstoffe. *Antonie van Leeuwenhoek*, **28**:141–160.

KOFFLER, HENRY
    1957.   Protoplasmic differences between mesophiles and thermophiles. *Bacteriol. Rev.*, **21**:227–240.

KUNZE, G.
    1817.   Zehn neue Pilzgattungen. *Mykologische Hefte*, **1**:1–18.

KÜSTER, EBERHARD, and ROMANO LOCCI
    1964.   Studies on peat and peat microorganisms II. Occurrence of thermophilic fungi in peat. *Arch. Mikrobiol.*, **48**:319–324.

LA TOUCHE, C. J.
    1950.   On a thermophile species of Chaetomium. *Trans. Brit. Mycol. Soc.*, **33**:94–104.

LENDNER, A.
    1929.   Détermination de Mucorinées. *Bull. Soc. Bot. Genève*, **21**:256–263.

LILLY, V. G., and H. L. BARNETT
    1951.   *Physiology of the Fungi.* xii & 464 pp. McGraw-Hill, New York.

LINDT, W.
    1886.   Mitteilungen über einige neue pathogene Schimmelpilze. *Arch. exp. Path. Pharmakol.*, **21**:269–298.

LING-YOUNG, M.
    1930.   Étude biologique des phénomènes de la sexualité chez les Mucorinées. *Rev. Gen. Bot.*, **42**:722–752.

LODDER, J., and N. J. W. KREGER-VAN RIJ
    1952.   *The Yeasts: A Taxonomic Study.* xi & 713 pp. Interscience, New York.

LOGINOVA, L. G., A. E. KOSMACHEV, R. S. GOLOVACHEVA and L. M. SEREGINA
    1962.   A study of the thermophilic microflora of Mount Yangan-Tau in the

southern Urals. *Microbiologiya*, **31**:1082–1086. (In Russian with English summary. A full translation into English appears in *Microbiology*, **31**:877–880.)

LOOMIS, W. F.
1957.   Sexual differentiation in Hydra. *Science*, **126**:735–739.

MAL'CHEVSKAYA, N. N.
1939.   Microbiological characteristics of some peats in the Leningrad district. *Trudy Pushkin Sel'skokhoz. Inst.*, **13**:5–38. (In Russian.)

MANNING, G. B., and L. L. CAMPBELL
1961.   Thermostable α-amylase of Bacillus stearothermophilus. I. Crystallization and some general properties. *J. Biol. Chem.*, **236**:2952–2957.

MANNING, G. B., L. L. CAMPBELL, and R. J. FOSTER
1961.   Thermostable α-amylase of Bacillus stearothermophilus. II. Physical properties and molecular weight. *J. Biol. Chem.*, **236**:2958–2961.

MASON, E. W.
1933.   Annotated account of fungi received at the Imperial Mycological Institute. List II (Fascicle 2), pp. 1–67. Imperial Mycological Institute, Kew.

MASON, E. W.
1941.   Annotated account of fungi received at the Imperial Mycological Institute. List II (Fascicle 3—Special Part), pp. 101–144. Imperial Mycological Institute, Kew.

MICHELI, PIERANTONIO
1729.   *Nova plantarum genera*. xxii & 234 pp. Bernardi Paperinii, Florence.

MIEHE, HUGO
1905.   Über die Selbsterhitzung des Heues. *Arb. deutsch. Landwirtsch.-Gesellsch.*, **111**:76–91. (Anhang zu: Falke, Friedrich. 1905. Die Braunheubereitung zugleich eine Schilderung der gebräuchlichsten Heubereitungsarten. zweite Aufl. *ibid.*, **111**:1–75.)

MIEHE, HUGO
1907a. *Die Selbsterhitzung des Heus. Eine biologische Studie*. pp. 1–127. Gustav Fischer, Jena.

MIEHE, HUGO
1907b. Thermoidium sulfureum n. g. n. sp., ein neuer Wärmepilz. *Ber deutsch. bot. Gesl.*, **25**:510–515.

MIEHE, HUGO
1930a. Die Wärmebildung von Reinkulturen im Hinblick auf die Ätiologie der Selbsterhitzung pflanzlicher Stoffe. *Arch. Mikrobiol.*, **1**:78–118.

MIEHE, HUGO
1930b. Über die Selbsterhitzung des Heues. 2e Aufl. *Arb. deutsch. Landwirtsch.-Gesellsch., Berlin*, **196**:1–47.

REFERENCES

MIGULA, WALTER
> 1934. *Kryptogamen-Flora von Deutschland, Deutsch-Österreich und der Schweiz.* Bd. 3. Pilze. Teil 4. Abt. 2. viii & 629 pp. In D. W. Thome, *Flora von Deutschland. Österreich und der Schweiz.* Bd. 11. Abt. 2. Akademische Verlagsges., Leipzig.

MILITZER, WALTER, T. B. SONDEREGGER, L. CONSTANCE TUTTLE, and C. E. GEORGI
> 1949. Thermal enzymes. *Arch. Biochem.*, **24**:75–82.

MILITZER, WALTER, L. CONSTANCE TUTTLE, and C. E. GEORGI
> 1951. Thermal enzymes. III. Apyrase from a thermophilic bacterium. *Arch. Biochem. Biophys.*, **31**:416–423.

MILNER, MAX, C. M. CHRISTENSEN, and W. F. GEDDES
> 1947. Grain storage studies. VI. Wheat respiration in relation to moisture content, mold growth, chemical deterioration and heating. *Cereal Chem.*, **24**:182–199.

MISHUSTIN, E. N.
> 1950. *Thermophilic Microorganisms in Nature and Practice.* 391 pp. Institute of Microbiology, Academy of Sciences, Moscow and Leningrad. (In Russian.)

MITCHELL, RODGER
> 1960. The evolution of thermophilous water mites. *Evolution*, **14**:363–377.

MOLISCH, HANS
> 1926. *Pflanzenbiologie in Japan.* x & 270 pp. Gustav Fischer, Jena.

MÜLLER, GUNTHER
> 1961a. Mikrobiologische Untersuchungen über die "Futterverpilzung durch Selbsterhitzung". I. Mitteilung. Orientierende Untersuchung eines laboratoriumsmässig angesetzten Schimmelfutters. *Zentralbl. Bakt. Parasitenk. Infekt.*, 2te Abt. **114**:192–202.

MÜLLER, GUNTHER
> 1961b. Mikrobiologische Untersuchungen über die "Futterverpilzung durch Selbsterhitzung". II. Mitteilung. Untersuchungen verschiedener verpilzte Futtermittel landwirtschaftlicher Betriebe. *Zentralbl. Bakt. Parasitenk. Infekt.*, 2te Abt. **114**:388–425.

NAUMOV, N. A.
> 1935. *Keys to the Mucorales* (2nd ed.). 136 pp. Izdatel'stvo Akademii Nauk SSSR, Moscow. (In Russian.)

NIELSEN, NIELS
> 1927. Fungi isolated from soil and from excrements of arctic animals derived from Disko and North-Greenland. *Meddelelser om Grønland*, **74**:1–8.

NIESE, GÜNTER
> 1959. Mikrobiologische Untersuchungen zur Frage der Selbsterhitzung organischer Stoffe. *Arch. Mikrobiol.*, **34**:285–318.

NOACK, KURT
   1912.   Beiträge zur Biologie der thermophilen Organismen. *Jahrb. wissensch.
           Bot.*, **51**:593–648.

NOACK, KURT
   1920.   Der Betriebstoffwechsel der thermophilen Pilze. *Jahrb. wissensch. Bot.*,
           59:413–466.

NORMAN, A. G.
   1930.   The biological decomposition of plant materials. Part III. Physiological
           studies on some cellulose-decomposing fungi. *Ann. Appl. Biol.*, **17**:575–
           613.

NORMAN, A. G., L. A. RICHARDS, and R. E. CARLYLE
   1941.   Microbial thermogenesis in the decomposition of plant materials. Part
           I. An adiabatic fermentation apparatus. *J. Bacteriol.*, **41**:689–697.

ODINTSOVA, E. N.
   1947.   Thermophilic yeast organism Endoblastomyces thermophilus nov. gen.,
           nov. sp. 1. Morphology and life cycle. *Mikrobiologiia*, **16**:273–284. (In
           Russian.)

OMVIK, AASA
   1955.   Two new species of Chaetomium and one new Humicola species.
           Mycologia, **47**:748–757.

OTANI, YOSHIO
   1931.   Vergleichende Studien über die Mucor Gattung II. Mitteilung. Über
           die Temperaturverhältnisse. *Trans. Tottori Soc. Agric. Sci.*, **3**:174–186.
           (In Japanese, with German summary.)

PALLMANN, H., K. HÜNI, and O. DÖNZ
   1945.   Der Wärmehaushalt und die Kontrolle überhitzter Futterstöcke. Zur
           Diagnose der Selbstentzündung von Dürrfutter- und Getreidestöcken.
           Schweiz. Landwirtsch. Monatshefte, **23**:223–243.

PERRIER, A.
   1929.   Sur la présence de certains champignons thermophiles dans le fumier
           et les matières organiques en décomposition. *C. R. Acad. Sci. Paris*,
           188:1426–1429.

PERSOON, C. H.
   1801.   *Synopsis methodica fungorum.* xxx & 708 pp. H. Dietrich, Göttingen.

PERSOON, C. H.
   1822.   *Mycologia Europaea.* Sect. 1. iv & 357 pp. J. J. Palm, Erlangen.

PLUM, N.
   1932.   Verschiedene Hyphomyceten-Arten als Ursache sporadischer Fälle von
           Abortus beim Rind. *Acta Path. Microbiol. Scandinav.*, **9**:150–157.

PRECHT, H., J. CHRISTOPHERSEN, and H. HENSEL
   1955.   *Temperatur und Leben.* xii & 514 pp. Springer-Verlag, Berlin.

RAPER, K. B.
   1957.   Nomenclature in Aspergillus and Penicillium. *Mycologia*, **49**:644–662.

RAPER, K. B., and CHARLES THOM
 1949.   A Manual of the Penicillia. ix & 875 pp. Williams & Wilkins, Baltimore.

REESE, E. T.
 1946.   Aerobic decomposition of cellulose by micro-organisms at temperatures
         above 40°C. iii & 100 pp. Unpublished Ph.D thesis, Pennsylvania State
         College, Evanston, Penn.

REGE, R. D.
 1927.   Bio-chemical decomposition of cellulosic materials, with special refer-
         ence to the action of fungi. Ann. Appl. Biol., 14:1–44.

REID, J. J., D. W. McKINSTRY, and D. E. HALEY
 1938.   Studies on the fermentation of tobacco. 2. Microorganisms isolated from
         cigar-leaf tobacco. Penn. Agric. Exp. Sta. Bull., 363:1–18.

RIVELLONI, G.
 1938.   Isolamento di un raro micete (Malbranchea Bolognesii-Chiurcoi) da
         una micosi umana. Boll. Sez. Reg. Suppl. Giorn. Ital. Derm. Sif., 16:384.
         (Abstract of a paper presented at a session held in 1937.)

RODE, L. J., J. W. FOSTER, and V. T. SCHUHARDT
 1947.   Penicillin production by a thermophilic fungus. J. Bacteriol., 53:565–
         566.

SACCARDO, P. A.
 1880.   Conspectus generum fungorum Italiae inferiorum. Michelia, 2:1–38.

SACCARDO, P. A.
 1882a. Fungi Gallici. Ser. IV. Michelia, 2:583–648.

SACCARDO, P. A.
 1882b. Sylloge fungorum omnium hucusque cognitorum. Vol. 1. xix & 766 pp.
         P. A. Saccardo, Padua.

SACCARDO, P. A.
 1886.   Sylloge fungorum omnium hucusque cognitorum. Vol. 4. 810 pp. P. A.
         Saccardo, Padua.

SACCARDO, P. A.
 1908.   Notae mycologicae. Ser. X. Ann. Mycol., 6:553–569.

SACCARDO, P. A.
 1913.   Notae mycologicae. Ser. XVI. Ann. Mycol., 11:312–325.

SACCARDO, P. A., and ALEX. TROTTER
 1913.   Sylloge fungorum omnium hucusque cognitorum. Vol. 22. 1612 pp.
         P. A. Saccardo, Padua.

SAMES, T.
 1900.   Zur Kenntnis der bei höherer Temperatur wachsenden Bakterien- und
         Streptothrixarten. Zeitschr. Hyg., 33:313–362.

SCHULZE, K. L.
 1962.   Continuous thermophilic composting. Appl. Microbiol., 10:108–122.

SETCHELL, W. A.
   1903.   The upper temperature limits of life. *Science* (n.s.), **17**:934–937.

SHAPOSHNIKOV, V., and A. MANTEIFEL
   1923.   On the morphology, physiology, and biology of a new fungus Penicillium arenarium n. sp. in connection with citric acid fermentation. 1. The thermophilic species Penicillium arenarium nov. sp., producing citric acid. *Trudy Nauchn. Khim.-Farm. Inst.*, **5**:3–27. (In Russian.)

SHIFRINE, M., and J. J. PHAFF
   1958.   On the isolation, ecology and taxonomy of Saccharomycopsis guttulata. *Antonie van Leeuwenhoek*, **24**:193–209.

SIE, E. H., HARRY SOBOTKA, and HERMAN BAKER
   1961.   Factor converting mesophilic into thermophilic micro-organisms. *Nature*, **192**:86–87.

SMITH, GEORGE
   1957.   Some new and interesting species of micro-fungi. *Trans. Brit. Mycol. Soc.*, **40**:481–488.

SOPP, O. J.
   1912.   Monographie der Pilzgruppe Penicillium mit besonderer Berücksichtigung der in Norwegen gefundenen Arten. *Videnskabs-Selskabets i Christiania, Skrifter, 1 Math.-Naturv. Kl.* 1912, No. 11. pp. i–vi and 1–208. (Now *Norske Videnskaps-akademi, Oslo.*)

ŠPAČEK, J.
   1953.   Studie o teplobytné mykofloře moravské. *Práce Moravsk. Akad. Věd Přírod., Brünn*, **25**:357–392.

ŠPAČEK, J.
   1954.   Studie o teplobytné mykofloře moravské (II). *Práce Česk. Akad. Věd, Brněnsk. Zák.*, **26**(8):1–32.

SPARROW, F. K., JR.
   1960.   *Aquatic Phycomycetes* (2nd ed.). xxv & 1187 pp. University of Michigan Press, Ann Arbor.

SPENCE, DAVID
   1930.   Cultivation and preparation of rubber in the United States. *Ind. Eng. Chem.*, **22**:384–387.

SPENCE, DAVID
   1933.   Rubber. U.S. Patent 1,918,671.

STOLLER, B. B., F. B. SMITH, and P. E. BROWN
   1937.   A mechanical apparatus for the rapid, high-temperature microbial decomposition of fibrous, cellulosic materials in the preparation of composts for mushroom cultures. *J. Amer. Soc. Agron.*, **29**:717–723.

SWARTZ, M. N., N. O. KAPLAN, and MARY E. FRECH
   1957.   Mechanism of "heat activation" of enzymes. pp. 61–70 in Johnson, F. H. (ed.), *Influence of Temperature on Biological Systems*. xiv & 275 pp.

THOM, CHARLES
   1930.   *The Penicillia*. xiii & 644 pp. Williams & Wilkins, Baltimore.

THOM, CHARLES, and EDWIN LEFEVRE
   1921.   Flora of corn meal. *J. Agr. Res.*, **22**:179–188.

TOGASHI, KOGO
   1949.   *Biological Characters of Plant Pathogens, Temperature Relations*. 478 pp. Meibundo, Tokyo.

TRAAEN, A. E.
   1914.   Untersuchungen über Bodenpilze aus Norwegen. *Nytt Mag. Naturv.*, **52**:19–121.

TROTTER, ALEX
   1931.   (*Saccardo's*) *Sylloge fungorum omnium hucusque cognitorum*. Vol. 25. 1093 pp. Saccardo heirs, Avellino.

TSCHERNIAK, W. S.
   1928.   Zur Lehre von den Broncho- und Pneumonomykosen der Pferde. *Arch. wissensch. prakt. Tierheilk.*, **57**:417–444.

TSIKLINSKAYA, P.
   1899.   Sur les mucédinées thermophiles. *Ann. Inst. Pasteur, Paris*, **13**:500–505.

TURPIN, P. J. F.
   1838.   Mémoire sur la cause et les effets de la fermentation alcoolique et acéteuse. *C. R. Acad. Sci. Paris*, **7**:369–402.

VELICH, A.
   1914.   Thermophile microorganisms. *Casopsis Lékarů Ceskych, Prague*, **53**:1026–1027. (In Czech.)

VOUK, T. V.
   1929.   On the origin of the thermal flora. *Proc. Internat. Congr. Plant Sci.* (Ithaca, New York, 1926), **2**:1176–1179.

VOUK, VALE
   1950.   *Grundriss zu einer Balneobiologie der Thermen*. 88 pp. Birkhäuser, Basel.

WAKSMAN, S. A., and T. C. CORDON
   1939.   Thermophilic decomposition of plant residues in composts by pure and mixed cultures of microorganisms. *Soil Sci.*, **47**:217–225.

WAKSMAN, S. A., T. C. CORDON, and N. HULPOI
   1939.   Influence of temperature upon the microbiological population and decomposition processes in composts of stable manure. *Soil Sci.*, **47**:83–113.

WAKSMAN, S. A., and F. C. GERRETSEN
   1931.   Influence of temperature and moisture upon the nature and extent of decomposition of plant residues by microorganisms. *Ecology*, **12**:33–60.

WAKSMAN, S. A., W. W. UMBREIT, and T. C. CORDON
   1939.   Thermophilic Actinomycetes and fungi in soils and in composts. *Soil Sci.*, **47**:37–61.

WEBLEY, D. M.
   1948a. Aerobic mesophilic bacteria in composts. *Nature,* **161**:174–175.

WEBLEY, D. M.
   1948b. The microbiology of composting. 1. The behaviour of the aerobic meso-
      philic bacterial flora of composts and its relation to other changes taking
      place during composting. *Proc. Soc. Appl. Bacteriol.,* **1947**:83–89. (See
      under *J. Appl. Bacteriol.*)

WEDBERG, S. E., and L. F. RETTGER
   1941. Factors influencing microbial thermogenesis. *J. Bacteriol.,* **41**:725–743.

WHEELER, H. E., and J. W. McGAHEN
   1952. Genetics of Glomerella. X. Genes affecting sexual reproduction. *Amer.
      J. Bot.,* **39**:110–119.

WHITE, W. L., and MARY H. DOWNING
   1953. Humicola grisea, a soil-inhabiting cellulolytic hyphomycete. *Mycologia,*
      45:951–963.

WINTER, GEORG
   1887. *Die Pilze Deutschlands, Oesterreichs und der Schweiz.* In L. Raben-
      horst, *Kryptogamen-Flora von Deutschland, Oesterreich und der
      Schweiz,* 2te Aufl. Bd. 1. Abt. 2. viii & 928 pp. Eduard Kummer, Leip-
      zig.

WOLF, F. A., and F. T. WOLF
   1947. *The Fungi.* Vol. 2. xii & 538 pp. Wiley, New York.

ZYCHA, H.
   1935. *Pilze II. Mucorineae.* In *Kryptogamenflora der Mark Brandenburg,*
      Bd. 6a, viii & 264 pp. Borntraeger, Leipzig.

INDEX

WARNER MEMORIAL LIBRARY
EASTERN COLLEGE
ST. DAVIDS, PA.   19087